Dear Diary

Dear Diary

CLAIRE HENNESSY

POOLBEG

Published 2000
by Poolbeg Press Ltd.
123 Grange Hill, Baldoyle
Dublin 13, Ireland
Email: poolbeg@poolbeg.com
www.poolbeg.com

The moral right of the author has been asserted.

5 7 9 10 8 6 4

A catalogue record for this book is available from the British Library.

ISBN 1-85371-917-X

Set by Rowland Phototypesetting Ltd, in 11.5/15.5 Goudy
Printed by Cox and Wyman, Reading, Berkshire.

ABOUT THE AUTHOR

Claire Hennessy was born on February 24th 1986 and lives in Knocklyon with her parents and younger brother. Her dad's into athletics and her mom is one of those people who can actually understand computers. She goes to Loreto High School, Beaufort, an all-girls' school in Rathfarnham which she wishes could be a mixed school. Her favourite subjects are (surprisingly, not English) Maths and Home Economics, although she's hopeless at cooking. She adores reading and writing, obviously - as long as it's not for homework! She loves "Ally McBeal", "Friends", "Dawson's Creek" as well as chocolate, shopping, anything purple, and smiley faces. She hates when shops run out of peanut M&Ms, the end of holidays, and being forced to tidy up. She wrote her first book when she was twelve in sixth class, like the girls in the book. She wrote her second book at thirteen and is currently working on a third. She doesn't have a clue what she wants to be when she grows up so she's hoping the writing thing goes well. Other possible career options are a lawyer in a court with an insane judge, a bad radio psychiatrist, or a glamorous wife to someone fabulously wealthy! (Dream on!)

Also by Claire Hennessy

DEDICATION

To all of my family and friends, everyone I know and love - this way I can't be accused of leaving anyone out

Prologue: Aisling

Saturday   *27th December*

The community centre was packed last night for the Christmas disco. Well, they called it the Christmas disco – they'd have been better off saying it was the St Stephen's Day disco, but that doesn't have the same ring to it, does it?

Nearly all of our class were there and we were messing around together. My friends and I were just standing around for a bit, sipping our cans of Coke, chatting about all the boys. Somehow this year they seem more human, and definitely much more approachable. For some of the girls it's never been a problem. Like Kate Long, for example. I'm not exactly sure what to think of her. She's really cool but she seems a bit aloof, if you ask me. Like she thinks she's better than everyone else. She's in the choir with me, but I've never really spoken to her. To be honest, she's a bit intimidating. I suppose she could just be quiet. If she wasn't so pretty and cool and athletic, that's exactly what I'd think of her. But she is all those things, so I have to say that she's looking down on us. I really have to get out of the habit of criticising people. I will try and be a nicer person, that'll be my New Year's Resolution.

Alison laughed hysterically when I told her that. She thinks I'm far too nice already. I'm not, really. Well, maybe I am. I usually see the best in people.

1

After the disco we sat around talking. Well, the girls did – the boys went off to beat each other up or something. We were waiting for our parents to collect us – it was too dark to walk home on your own. And of course there had been some mistake on the tickets, saying it finished at half-eleven instead of eleven, so we had to wait.

One of the questions that came up was about who kept a diary. It was really surprising, actually. Kate and I were the first two to say "yes". Huh. Hers is probably full of detailed descriptions of clothes or something. Now, now, Aisling, be a nicer person. Well, there's a couple of days left this year, I can be as bitchy as I want.

Anyway, then Amy and Megan put up their hands at the same time. Typical. They're best friends, crazy, mad, insane, and I get along so well with both of them. Then Alison said she had a diary too but of course I knew that. She's my best friend, after all.

The other questions were basically all about boys and who'd met who, at which point Alison and I edged away slightly. Because we haven't met anyone. But it turned out not to matter – hardly anyone has. Kate said she hadn't. I bet she was lying. I'm so suspicious of her! I don't know why, there's just something about her that I don't really like. I can't explain it.

1: Aisling's Diary

Fact-File

Name:: Aisling Molloy (pronounced "Ashling")

Age:: 12 (13 on May 9th)

Family:: Mum, Dad, little brother Henry

Looks:: dark hair, green eyes

Hobbies:: singing in the school choir, playing the recorder and keyboard, reading

Ambitions:: To be a musician in a famous orchestra

School:: At Hillside Primary, will be going to Loreto Secondary in September

Friends:: Megan, Alison, Amy, Kate, Emma

Worst Enemies:: None

Favourite T.V. programmes:: Friends, Veronica's Closet, Father Ted, Suddenly Susan

Favourite Actor:: Leonardo DiCaprio!!!

Favourite Actress:: Kate Winslet

Favourite Film:: Titanic

Favourite Book:: Sisters . . . no way!

Favourite Author:: Siobhán Parkinson

Favourite Singer:: Celine Dion

Favourite Group:: Eternal

Favourite Song:: My Heart Will Go On

Favourite Albums:: Titanic soundtrack, Celine Dion's Let's Talk About Love, the Eternal Greatest Hits album

My friends and I want to go and see Titanic together, so we started talking about it today in yard and decided we'd like to see it next Monday, up in the Square. Megan's dad can drive us. Amy and I are going for just one reason – the incredibly gorgeous and sexy Leonardo DiCaprio. And there's a terrific love theme – My Heart Will Go On, by Celine Dion, who's my favourite singer. The song is so beautiful – I love singing it. Megan got me to sing it for her today. She says I'm a brilliant singer, but that's the sort of thing you have to say to your best friends. She's a good singer as well, we're both in the school choir, in the descants – that's soprano, by the way.

There's only two weeks and two days until the week-long school skiing trip starts. I'm going, same as Megan and Emma. A whole week in Italy, skiing – my kind of trip, especially when you miss a week of school as well! We plan on sharing a room together.

Emma's looking forward to the trip more than any of us. She's been skiing before, and she's really good at it. She's really sporty and fit. Completely unlike me. I'm the musical one – as well as singing in the choir, I play the keyboard and recorder.

Megan and Amy are definitely the funny ones, as well as Megan being a great actress and Amy being great at art. Then there's Alison. She's really smart, and she writes all these terrific stories and does incredibly well in school. Sometimes I get jealous of her, even though she's one of my best friends and I've known her forever.

Mrs Lyons was out today. I was put into a fifth class with Alison and Vicki Simons. Alison and I sat at the back. I felt sort of sorry for Vicki, sitting up at the front of the classroom all by herself. Alison says I'm way too sensitive for my own good. Maybe she's right, but it's just the way I am.

Alison and I finished our work before our first break at eleven and then we were able to talk quietly for the rest of the day. I wonder how Amy, Emma and Megan got on. They were together in a fourth class. I bet they got into trouble. When Amy and Megan get together they get totally crazy. They always seem to have so much fun.

I had choir practice after school, like I do every Wednesday afternoon. Megan and I were talking to Kate Long. She's very nice, in our class, she's very sporty, a good friend of Emma's. At one point, when we were talking about TV programmes, she looked like she was going to cry. I've a feeling I know what's wrong. Her dad died of a heart attack about a month ago. I remember we all sort of tiptoed around her when she came back into school after the funeral. I sent her a note saying how sorry I was and if she ever wanted someone to talk to, she knows where to go. Anyway, she's been acting like she's completely recovered, but she can't have. I feel so sorry for her. Sometimes I see her in class and she's keeping up her cool image, but I can sort of tell she feels depressed. I've wanted to talk with her and see if she's really okay, but I've always felt sort of intimidated by her. She's really nice to me, though, it's not her fault. It's just that she's so popular and not only that but Conor

Jeffries, who is only the most gorgeous guy in our class, fancies her like mad. It's so obvious. Conor's really nice, he does really well in school, is great at all sports, and he's way more sensitive than most boys. I remember in fourth class, Alison and I both had huge crushes on him and used to spend hours talking about him.

Thursday   12th February

I am so depressed. I forgot to do my English reading last night, and Mrs Lyons got really mad and started yelling like crazy at me. And I couldn't help it, I just started crying, and it was really embarrassing, but then luckily the bell rang for yard so I was off the hook.

Alison and Megan were being really nice to me, but my ex-friends Amy and Emma were jeering me. I'm never talking to them again. I mean, if either of them were really upset, we'd all be really nice to them. I hate people like that. Sometimes I feel like snapping at them for that, because they really annoy me when they have double standards, but I know I'd make a fool of myself and they wouldn't get it, anyway. God, I hate my life.

Friday   13th February

As it turns out, Emma and Amy were feeling really guilty about being so bitchy yesterday. They came over to me, Megan, and Alison today to apologise. I'm glad everything's okay again, I hate fighting with my friends.

Just two hours until the Valentine's Disco! I can't wait.

We plan to just hang around together and have fun but if a certain someone – James Robinson from my class – turns up, I think I just might hang around him!

Saturday   *14th February*

Last night was absolutely terrific! I arrived with my friends and then I saw James. I smiled at him and he came over to me and asked if I wanted to dance. Naturally, I said yes. Then we danced again and again and then the slow songs came on and everyone started getting off with everyone else. So – if you can't beat 'em, join 'em, and James is a terrific kisser . . .

He asked if I was going with anyone and would I be embarrassed hanging around someone like him!! I said, why would I be embarrassed? He said that it's just that I'm so pretty and smart and talented (yes, ME!) that no one expects me to go out with someone from sixth class.

In a few words, I got my first kiss – hey, I know it's a bit late! – I'm now going with James, and I had a GREAT TIME! I feel so . . . I don't know, teenage. I know that half the girls in my class have been meeting boys for years, including Emma, Amy, and probably Kate, but I've never really gotten into it.

Monday   *16th February*

I've just got back from Titanic – it was brilliant! Alison and I were crying practically the whole time, and then Megan joined in when the boat started to sink. We got kind of giddy after a while, from crying so much! Amy and Emma pretended they didn't know us.

Alison had some great news today. Her thirteenth birthday is on the sixth of March, and she's getting to go on the skiing trip! Her mum secretly paid for it and has been kept informed about everything.

It's going to be so much fun with the four of us. I just wish Amy could go as well. I bet she's feeling left out. I don't think anyone else realises it – sometimes I get really annoyed the way some of my friends can be so insensitive.

Friday   *20th February*

I'm over at Megan's house right now, for her slumber birthday party. We've just watched Romy And Michelle's High School Reunion and we're about to start watching Now And Then.

So far it's been great. We've talked about everything and had loads of fun. Usually we have fights when the five of us have sleepovers, because we can't agree on anything, but so far that hasn't happened.

Thursday   *26th February*

All the people who were going on the trip – about forty altogether – came in with tons of luggage. Me, Alison, Megan and Emma said bye to Amy before a coach came to take us to Dublin Airport. Alison and I sat together in the coach, in front of Megan and Emma.

The flight to the international airport in Milan took

about two and a half hours. I was really excited, but also nervous, because I'd never been on a plane before. I was really scared at the start, and I was practically crying, but Alison reassured me.

Once we arrived, we got our bags and went straight to the ski resort.

You should see the room I'm sharing with Megan, Emma and Alison. It's huge, with two wardrobes, an en suite bathroom, and a bunk bed plus two other beds. Megan has the top bunk, Emma has the bottom one, and me and Alison are in the other beds.

For today, we get to relax, get used to the place, and then tomorrow we hit the slopes!

Friday   27th February

I hate it here! I was hopeless at skiing today and made a complete fool of myself by falling over practically every two seconds. Tears were welling up in my eyes every few minutes, but everyone was just getting irritated with me, waiting impatiently for their turn, which made me feel even worse. Then guess what was for dinner. OCTOPUS! Some people had it and actually liked it. I tried it and almost threw up.

I hate it so much. After dinner I went straight back to the room on my own and just lay down on my bed and cried.

Alison's being really nice to me – she knows I'm upset. I'm glad she's here. It's nice to know that someone actually cares – that someone actually notices!

Saturday   28th February

Emma broke her arm today when someone crashed into her when she was skiing.

I'm not going to go skiing tomorrow. I'll say I'm sick.

What I really hate is that I was really looking forward to this trip. I wish I was at home, missing half of the work because of choir practices. The choir is going to the Córfhéile na Scoileanna on Tuesday. I wish I could be there, singing. It's my last year in the choir – I wish I hadn't gone on this trip. I'd be with Amy in a classroom, messing around, having fun with James, and practising the songs for the Córfhéile with the rest of the choir.

Sunday   1st March

I told Mrs Lyons I was sick today, and I confessed to my friends that I just didn't want to go skiing. I really don't. Maybe they think I'm scared. I suppose I am, but of making an idiot of myself. At least Alison didn't complain about me deserting her – which, by the way, I feel really guilty about. But she told me she went up to the higher group today with Megan, so that's okay.

First of all this morning, Emma and I went down to the café for some sweets and a drink. That was at about ten-thirty. We spent lots of lira on sweets.

Then we went to the games room. Orla Smith, the girl who crashed into Emma yesterday, was there. Her ankle's all bandaged up. The three of us were the only ones there and took turns playing against each other on the PlayStation.

We got bored of that after a while, so at about one o' clock we went for a snack and then we went into the viewing-room. They were showing Titanic, and it was just starting, so we sat down on the floor – you can sit on the chairs, sofas, or the carpeted floor – and watched the film. We were sitting in a pile of cushions and I had to look like I wasn't crying – which I was!

It finished at about four-thirty, and we had dinner soon after. We sat at our usual table for four, except Megan was with Alan Young, who she fancies like crazy, so Emma invited Orla to sit with us.

Today was the first day I enjoyed myself on this trip.

Monday   2nd March

Into Milan today for shopping. I spent almost the whole lot of my money – tons of lira – on souvenirs and so on. We were split up into groups of five and six, with a teacher for each of us. I was put with Emma, Alison, Megan, and Orla, with Mrs Lyons supervising us.

There was this cool shop called "Europe" which sold all sorts of things from all the European countries – they even had Irish shamrock keyrings! I got a present for Henry there – he's eight, so I got him sweets! – and I got my parents a box of Belgian chocolates.

I bought Amy a silver bracelet with European emblems hanging off it. I hope she likes it.

Tuesday   *3rd March*

Today Megan and Alison convinced me to go skiing again. I was in the cable car as it took us up the mountain and I looked down and I was just so scared, you wouldn't believe it. I burst into tears and I said I just couldn't do this. Alison held me and calmed me down. I had to force myself not to look down.

I was really scared and as soon as I was back at the resort I went up to the room and cried. Which I seem to be spending a lot of this holiday doing.

At lunch, Alison and Megan came up to the room and saw how miserable I was. Alison offered to skip her afternoon skiing session so that she could stay with me and cheer me up, but I told her not to. I'd have felt really guilty otherwise.

Emma wanted me to come down with her the games room, but I told her I'd be fine. Alison said I could read any of the books she'd brought with her, so I picked one out and spent the rest of the afternoon reading. She's really been a great help, if she wasn't here I don't know what I'd do.

Sometimes I start to think I over-reacted this morning, then I remember how scary it was. I can't wait until I'm back in Ireland again.

Wednesday   *4th March*

I said I still felt sick this morning, and I even told my friends that. I hated lying, but they probably all think I'm a big wimp. How can I tell them how scared I am?

Last night I felt so miserable I just cried myself to sleep. Megan came over to me – she was still awake, and I hadn't even noticed – and she just sat beside for a while and we talked quietly. She said she understood if I was scared of going on the cable car because of the height – which I am – because she was too, on the first day we went skiing. Then she dragged herself over back to her own bed. I felt better after that, like I wasn't being a total baby about it. Still, I remembered being on the cable car, and I got upset again.

The disco's tonight, for us and the other schools that are at the resort. I don't think I'll go.

Later

I went to the disco, but it was so boring that I didn't think I could stand the full three hours. The level of supervision was unbelievable. Me and Alison went back to our room and talked. Megan and Alan went off somewhere, and Emma and Orla were messing someplace as well.

We leave tomorrow at around eleven. I can't wait!

Thursday   5th March

We're on the plane now. We left the resort at eleven-thirty and went by coach to Milan. We had to check in our luggage and everything and we went into the Duty Free shop before we boarded the plane.

Later

All the parents were waiting in the airport when we arrived. Amy showed up as well, with Emma's mum. We all hugged her and then pounced on her for information about the week we were gone. There were a few kids from the class who were hanging around together – as well as Amy, there was James, Helen Murray, Kate, Trevor White and Conor. Apparently they had a great time. And I'm glad one of my best friends was around James so that I know he wasn't flirting with any of the girls. Amy wouldn't let them!

Saturday   *7th March*

Just back from Alison's slumber party. Amy got her presents that we brought back to her as well as Alison getting her birthday presents.

We watched Romeo And Juliet, the one with Claire Danes and the incredibly gorgeous Leonardo DiCaprio. It was so hard to understand, though – you needed a dictionary to get it!

Monday   *9th March*

Today there was an extra-long choir practice. Normally the choir practises for an hour after school, on Wednesdays, but with the Confirmations coming up, we have practices almost every day during school, so Megan and I are missing at least one subject every day. Mrs Lyons says we have to try and catch up, so I get Alison to tell me what I've missed, and Megan's . . . well, being Megan. Sorry about saying this, but Megan doesn't really take school seriously.

Tuesday   10th March

We had a school assembly today. The teachers want us to put on a school play. First they need a student to write it. It's going to be so cool. I might try out, but I'm not that good at acting. Megan is, and Amy's quite good, but I'm too shy.

There are some people I can think of who are good enough to write the play. But it has to be written by the end of this month! No one could write a whole long play that fast – especially with Confirmation this month.

Wait. There is someone in sixth class who could manage it. Alison! Duh. She could probably do it in a week, she's so brainy.

Monday   16th March

Our Confirmation was today. I did two singing solos.

It's official – Alison's writing the play. The fifth and sixth classes voted last week and it was practically unanimous. But get this – it's going to have music as well, and she wants some original stuff. So guess who she wants to write some songs and music for it? ME! I've done music for ages, but am I good enough to write lots of songs?

I was talking to the choir teacher, Miss Devlin, and she says she thinks I'm definitely good enough to do it, and she offered to help. So now me and Alison are practically totally responsible for the school play! It feels great, but it's also a lot of responsibility. I just hope we can handle it, and not mess it up or anything.

Wednesday *18th March*

Well, today Alison was telling Mrs Lyons about me writing music and lyrics for the play, and she was really pleased that it's going to be a musical. She asked us if we could have it finished by the end of March and we said, yes, we think so.

I had practically no work to do today in the school. The other two sixth classes were making their Confirmations today, and the choir were singing. So at ten o' clock Megan and I had to go to a practice, then at eleven the Confirmation service started. It lasted until one o' clock, and then anyone who was in the choir was allowed leave at that time. As a reward for putting in so much effort and so on.

Life is good when you're thirteen
Not many problems, or so it seems
But at least when your parents are nagging you
Or kids are slagging you
Your friends are always there for you

Teachers can give out to you no end
Siblings can drive you round the bend
And as for boyfriends, don't even ask
It's too complicated and confusing a task
At least your friends are always there for you

Of course, if there's a really cute boy
And none of your friends are all that coy
They're all over him as fast as you can see

And then you think, "Hey, why me?"
What was that about friends being there for you?

That's one of the songs I wrote for the play. I tried singing it lots of different ways before I wrote the music for it. Alison loves it. It's not exactly fine opera, but it's perfect for the play. According to Alison, anyway.

Later

> Who needs boys, anyway?
> They demand too much time
> They're selfish and annoying
> And they say, "Girl, you're MINE"
>
> Who needs boys, anyway?
> They do stupid things
> Like giving you those gross sweets
> Or those totally tacky earrings!
>
> Who needs boys, anyway?
> They can be such a pain
> But if I had a choice,
> I'd pick him as a boyfriend again.

That's a song I just came up with. I was inspired after . . . well, James dumped me. You see, we had this fight . . . He said I was spending way too much time on the play, and that I didn't even bother talking to him anymore, etc., etc. I said that he was being selfish and inconsiderate etc. Anyway, we got into this huge fight and we're not going together anymore.

The thing is, I think James is using my involvement in the play as an excuse. You know what I really think? That he likes someone else. It's probably someone he was with when I was skiing . . . Helen or Kate. Only I hate to think it's Kate, because she's always been really friendly to me. But Helen's too quiet and shy for him, he always says he likes girls who "know what they want". Anyway, she fancies Trevor, it's obvious. Maybe I'm just over-reacting.

Thursday   19th March

Amy is acting so weird! Today a pile of us were talking about the play, during yard time, except it was raining so we had to stay in the classroom, and everyone crowded into one corner.

Anyway, James was sitting near me, and he was chatting to Amy, you know the way they're friends. Amy saw me looking at the two of them and she made some excuse and hurried off.

What could be wrong with her? Maybe she thinks I think she's trying to move in on James, and that I'd be hurt because, after all, me and James only broke up, well, yesterday!

But wait. That doesn't make sense. I've only told Alison and Megan that I broke up with him. I haven't told Amy or Emma about it yet. So . . . what's up with Amy and James?

Wednesday   25th March

Megan got her period today in school. She told me, no one else, and I felt awkward. I don't know what it is, I just can't talk about that sort of stuff without getting embarrassed. I wonder what it feels like, though.

Friday   27th March

It's almost midnight but I want to write down what happened tonight. I went over to Amy's house, and Helen was there as well, and the three of us watched TV for a while. It turned out Helen was spending the night, and I went back home for a while to ask my parents could I sleep over and I got my stuff.

When I got back, it was about eight-thirty, and we decided to go out for supplies before it got dark. The newsagents is just around the corner from Amy's house.

We were walking past the end house, and we could hear the loud music from across the road. Obviously there was a party of some sort going on. (Just call me Sherlock Holmes for figuring that out.)

Just then, Kate hurried out. When she saw us she ran across to us.

"Everyone's drinking in there," she said breathlessly. "Emma and Orla are in there. I think they're drunk. And one of those guys tried to rip off my clothes," she added. She looked like she was going to cry.

Emma and Orla staggered out then, singing tunelessly and bumping into each other.

We walked home with them, holding onto them so that they didn't collapse. We explained to Emma's mum and Orla's parents about it, and Kate added that some of the older kids hadn't told them that the drink was alcoholic. I think they were mostly worried about the chance that they'd tried drugs, but Kate said, "No way, absolutely not."

Kate broke down crying after we made sure Emma and Orla had gotten home. She slept over at Amy's as well. She had been supposed to sleep over at Orla's, but, well . . .

Anyway, Amy, Helen and I comforted Kate and kept on checking that she was okay all night. Helen and Kate are both really nice. It's funny, I've been in the same class as them for ages and I never knew how nice they were. Helen's so quiet, you can never tell what she's thinking. And Kate's really nice, but when she's with Emma and Orla she can get really bitchy.

Saturday   *28th March*

You know, it's funny. I don't really miss James at all. Alison would say that I just liked the idea of James more than James himself. She's probably right.

Speaking of Alison, she's totally flipping out about the play. It's supposed to be ready by the end of this month, but I'd say the teachers wouldn't mind if it was in a few days late. It's a good thing I don't need to have the music ready for another few weeks.

Anyway, I was over at her house. We were in the study, with her typing furiously on the computer, and me writing some lyrics for the tune I'd written earlier on, and she suddenly burst into tears.

"I can't have this ready in two days," she sobbed. "I just can't."

It was a pretty big shock. I mean, Alison always seems really in control, and she absolutely never cries.

She hopped off the chair beside the computer and flopped down on the couch beside me.

"Think the teachers'll mind if the play's a few days late?" she asked me weakly.

I smiled at her. "Don't worry about it! Make up some excuse."

"Yeah."

"Hey, let's go call for Megan and Amy so that they can act out that scene you just wrote."

We called over to Amy's house first, and Megan and Kate were there as well. So the three of them came back to Alison's house, and they acted out the scene for us, with Megan as Samantha, Amy as Helen, and Kate as Liz.

Actually, now that I think about it, that might be the way it works out when the play is performed. Alison and I are helping Miss Devlin and Mr Fitzsimons choose who gets the different parts. And Megan is undoubtedly the best actress in the school. And she and Amy have acted out lots of the scenes. Plus, Kate is really good at the part of Liz. She's really skinny as well, which makes it more realistic (In the play, Liz has bulimia and she's really thin).

I've been teaching Megan the songs. The part of Samantha requires being able to sing soprano. There're five songs Megan will have to sing if she gets the part.

Anyway, Alison and I get to recommend anyone we think should get the part before the audition, and we plan to recommend Megan, Amy and Kate. As well as them being the best for the part, it'd be so much fun with the five of us together.

Sunday   29th March

Our next-door neighbours finally sold their house. They've had the For Sale sign up for months now. They want to move into a bigger house – the houses in our estate are four-bedroomed, which is big enough, but the couple next door have twin three-and-a-half-year-olds, a two-year-old, and the mother's pregnant again.

Anyway, my dad was talking to them, and they've found a buyer. They'll be moving out in a few weeks, and then the new family will be moving in. Maybe there'll be someone my own age, you never know.

Monday   30th March

Alison handed in the play today. She must've been working all day yesterday to get it done, because she had about another fifteen pages to do on Saturday.

The next-door neighbours, the Feldmans, the ones who are selling the house, were talking to me this morning, just before I left for school. They're going out – just the parents – on Friday night, for dinner, to celebrate the house being sold. Anyway, they need someone to look after the kids from about seven to eleven-thirty, and they'd asked the girl across the road, who couldn't do it, so they asked me. I said, "Yeah, sure, as long as my parents let me." You know, because it's a bit late – eleven-thirty! But I went back inside to ask Mum, and she said, "Sure, honey" as it's on a Friday and it's only next-door, anyway.

Tuesday   31st March

Why can't I be thin
And gorgeous and smart
Why can't I be musical
Or good at drama or art?

I feel like no one
Will ever like me
I'm fat and I'm ugly
Oh, I hate being me

Why are all my friends
So much better than me?
How come they can get boyfriends
And not me?

I hate being ugly
And don't say I'm not
I know the truth
I know what's what.

Will anyone special
Ever like me?

I'm fat, I'm ugly
I hate being me.

That song's for the play, to be sung by whoever plays Liz.
I know Kate's a good singer, because I've heard her singing
in the choir. I hope she gets the part.

Megan's being very secretive and quiet. Something's up.
I asked Alison, but she doesn't know. Typical. I hate to
say this, but lately Alison has been a total bitch! I mean
it. She's so involved in the play she's forgotten there are
other things in the world.

Wednesday   1st April

I handed in all the music for the play today. I didn't expect
to have it finished so soon. But I'm glad to have it out of
the way.

We had a counsellor in today. It was only for sixth class.
Our counsellor was called Rebecca and she was really nice.
She talked to us about all sorts of stuff. The only thing is,
the whole class, boys and girls, were together, so it was kind
of embarrassing for us girls to ask questions about periods
and all that. Actually, it was incredibly embarrassing!

It lasted almost the whole day. We talked about all the
changes that happen in puberty, wet dreams (gross, I'm glad
I'm not a boy), periods, sex, etc. She actually wrote up a
list of names kids our age are called if we don't go out to
discos all the time and get off with the opposite sex. When
Mrs Lyons came in to get her handbag she practically had
a fit. The principal came in later, and that was when there

were pictures of both boys' and girls' "genitals". He quickly went out!

At break, most of the girls in our class stood around together and we asked each other if we'd got our periods yet. I haven't, yet, but I keep on getting this creamy-white stuff in my pants which Rebecca says means that I'm going to get it soon.

Thursday   2nd April

Today has just been one of those days. Megan is acting all secretive, Amy is unusually quiet and goes around with a guilty expression on her face, and all Alison can think about is the play. Plus Henry is really getting on my nerves by insisting that I 'fight' with him, (Ninja-style) and Mrs Lyons gave us a ton of homework and was really grumpy today. I was feeling just so . . . well, alone, because all my friends were acting weirdly, and I just wished the day could be over so I could go home, rush through my homework, and then sit around reading, or listening to music, or watching TV.

We've all been assigned a partner and a project to do over the next month or so. I was put with Helen, Amy and Emma are together, Alison is with Kate, and Megan is with Orla. Helen is really nice, as I've said before.

Friday   3rd April

Oh my God. Oh my God. I have just met this amazing boy. And he's moving in next door!

I was babysitting next-door, for the three kids. There's Kirsty and Nora, the three-and-half-year-old twins, and then there's the two-year-old, Luke. I had to put Luke to bed at seven-thirty, and the twins at eight-thirty.

Anyway, it was about eight o' clock, and Luke had finally gone to sleep. Kirsty was jumping all over the place and Nora was sitting quietly, sucking her thumb. I was reading a story to her when the doorbell rang. I gently lifted her off my knee and onto the beanbag in the corner, and went to get it.

I opened the door and there stood the most amazing, drop-dead gorgeous boy I had ever seen. And I mean gorgeous. As in, forget-about-Leonardo DiCaprio-gorgeous!

"Um, hi," he said, a bit awkwardly. "My mum sent me over here to pick up her keys. She left them here earlier on when she was talking to Mr Feldman about the house."

"Oh, hi," I said, fighting to stay cool. "You must be moving in here, right? I'm Aisling. I live next door. I'm just babysitting the kids."

"Oh, well, um, do you mind if I get the keys?"

"Sure. No problem. Come on in."

He walked in, and I followed him. "Are those them?" I asked, spotting a pair of keys lying on the counter.

"Mm-hmm." He looked out the kitchen window. "Oh, great, now it's starting to rain. Just what I need."

"Did you walk?"

"Yeah."

"Oh. Well, it'll probably stop soon. You can stay here for a while if you like."

"Are you sure? I mean, you won't get in trouble or anything?"

"Don't worry about it, okay?"

"Okay. Oh, by the way, I'm Kevin. Kevin Quinn."

"Well, you already know who I am. Here, can I get you anything? Biscuit, Coke?"

"No thanks."

"WAAAH!" That came from the playroom.

I hurried in there. Kirsty had whacked her ankle against the leg of a chair.

"It hurts, Aisling, it hurts!" she wailed.

I picked her up and checked out her ankle. It looked okay – no blood, no bruise starting to appear, nothing sprained or broken.

"It's okay, Kirsty, it's okay," I said.

"Is she okay?" Kevin asked from behind me.

"Mm-hmm."

"Kevin!" Nora screamed, throwing herself at him.

"Hiya, Nora. Has Aisling been strangling you or anything?"

I pretended to be offended. "I don't strangle children. I might kill them and then I'd end up like Louise Woodward."

"Good point," he grinned. Nora clambered up onto his shoulders.

Anyway, the point is, he stayed for about half an hour. This is what I found out about him – he's fourteen, and in second year. He likes P.E. and Spanish. He has a younger sister, aged four. He doesn't have a girlfriend!!!!!!

But maybe he thinks I'm too young for him. There is a two-year difference, after all. I don't think I actually told him I was twelve, but I'm sure it looks obvious.

I fancy him like CRAZY!!!!

Saturday   *4th April*

Amy just called. You will NOT believe this. I forgot I
hadn't told her about breaking up with James. So, he was
trying to ask her out and all that, and there she was feeling
really guilty because she thought James and I were still
going together! I can't believe it. Normally these things get
around really fast.

"No, I don't mind that you two are going out," I told
her. "Anyway, there's this absolutely positively gorgeous
guy – he's fourteen! – his name's Kevin, and he's moved
in next door, and I think he likes me, only he might think
I'm too young."

"I'm sure he thinks you're very mature for your age. You
act and look it, anyway. Hey, have you talked to Megan
since yesterday?"

"No. I called, but her dad said –"

"That she was 'out', right?"

"Yeah."

"Something's definitely up. I'm calling Alison. See ya."

"See ya."

I don't think something's up with Megan. I'd say she's
off with Alan somewhere.

Monday   *6th April*

Good thing I wasn't in school today, because I got my
period today. I felt something sort of dripping, then I went
into the bathroom and there was a reddish-brown stain in
my pants.

I haven't told Mum yet. It's just too embarrassing to bring up, and she'd get all, "Well, aren't you a woman now" and all that. Mum and I are not close and it would just be too uncomfortable.

Tuesday   7th April

Today I am in an extremely bad mood. My stomach is killing me. As if that wasn't enough Henry is really getting on my nerves. He is such a brat. I wanted to practise on my keyboard. He came in and started throwing himself around the room, knocking over my music stand and sending sheets flying, crashing into my desk and causing my CDs to fall onto the floor, and finally knocking the big pile of books I had on my locker onto my bed.

"Out! OUT! Before I KILL you!" I yelled.

"Yeah yeah whatever," he muttered. That's his new technique.

"No, NOT 'yeah yeah whatever'." I lifted him up and literally threw him out of my room.

I hate having a little brother.

Plus, I phoned Megan's house today. Her dad said she was out. I was talking to Orla in the shop today and she hasn't been able to get in touch with her either. She must be spending a lot of time with Alan or something.

Sunday   12th April

I am going to weigh at least a tonne by the time I finish all my Easter eggs. I got one from Mum and Dad, and one from Henry. I saw some of my relatives yesterday and today, and that produced another five Easter eggs. And I got four from my friends.

I felt awful on Wednesday, I had really bad back pains, because of my period. It ended on Thursday, thank God. I don't know why I was so anxious to get it. I really don't. Basically all it is is blood soaking through pads, ruining your pants, for ages and ages. God, if I have to put up with this for the next forty years I'll kill myself.

Tuesday   *14th April*

The "Easter recreational programme" started today. It'll continue until Saturday.

True-confession time today. Megan filled us in on why she was un-contact-able for the last week. She was in Paris. Visiting her mother.

Her mother? Yep, that's what I said too. Her mother – we never talk about Megan's mother. She left when Megan was three or four, and never wrote or visited or anything. Anyway, Megan went to visit her in Paris, and they had a great time, and they're going to keep in contact from now on. Etc etc.

Today, I signed up for my favourite class – music. I'm going to sign up for it tomorrow, because they do different things every day. I also signed up for art, tennis, hockey, and drama.

Wednesday   *15th April*

Drama at Hillside! It feels like I'm living in a soap or something. Today, we went swimming in the morning, which took up two sessions. When we got back it was time for lunch. We get an hour for lunch.

Most of us were out in the yard, and I went in to our classroom, which is just inside the door, and was being used for people to leave their coats and meet up in the morning and everything, to get my jacket.

Conor was in there. "Aisling, I need your help," he said as soon as I came in. "Kate's locked herself in the toilet."

"Oh my God, what happened?" I asked.

"I think Tricia Hanley said something about her dad."

"That bitch!" I exclaimed. I mean, really, that is a really rotten thing to do, to comment about Kate's dead dad. And knowing how sensitive Kate is . . . No wonder Kate's in there."

I knocked on the door of the bathroom. "Kate?" I asked gently. "Will you come out?"

She wouldn't answer. Conor and I took turns trying, but she stayed quiet.

"I wonder if she's okay in there," Conor said. 'Maybe she fainted, or hit her head or something . . ."

I put my finger up to my lips, telling him to be quiet. I pressed my ear against the door. I could hear movement in there, definitely.

"She's okay, I think," I said.

Conor looked really worried. He really cares about Kate, you can tell.

31

"Maybe if we got Emma, or Orla . . ." I wondered.

"No!" screamed Kate.

"Okay, scratch that," I muttered. Then I said, "Kate, are you going to come out now?"

The door swung open. "Hi," she said. She wasn't crying, but she had been, her eyes were all red around the edges.

"What happened?" Conor asked her gently. He sounded so sweet, so concerned. I wish I could find a boyfriend like that. Which reminds me of Kevin. I wonder when he's moving in.

Anyway, Kate and Conor did the sappy routine, and then Conor went off to play basketball.

"You're so lucky," I told Kate.

"I know," she smiled. "He really, you know, cares about me. Not like most of the other boys in our class."

We were in the classroom for a while, talking. Then Kate went into the bathroom again. When she came out, her face was bright red.

"Aisling . . . do you have any . . . you know . . ."

I unzipped my schoolbag, which I'd used for my swimming bag. The Always pads were still there, tucked away in the front pocket. I handed her one.

"Thanks," she said gratefully. "Have you . . ."

"Yeah. Only once."

"Mm-hmm. This is my second time."

We smiled at each other. Then Kate went in to the bathroom again.

Friday   *17th April*

Alison loaned me this book, a Judy Blume one, that I'd never read, even though I thought I'd read all of them. And I know why I haven't read this one – it is very Young Adult. It has detailed sex! It's called Forever. I'd better not let my parents see it.

My parents are having the Quinns over for dinner on Saturday, to "welcome them to our area". That includes Kevin! They're also having Lauren Taylor and Chris Walsh over, so Alison and Megan will be coming over as well. I just hope I'll get to spend some time with Kevin.

Saturday   *18th April*

Actually it's Sunday, but it's something like 1 a.m., so it still feels like Saturday. Megan and Alison understood when I explained about Kevin, so they went up to my room and when Kevin arrived I invited him into the playroom. Henry was, thankfully, in bed, if not asleep, so he was out of the way. We played computer games, and games on the Nintendo 64 (Henry's ninth birthday present, he was nine last week), and then we talked a bit.

"So, you're – how old? Fourteen?" That was him asking me.

"No, actually," I muttered, looking down at the floor.

"Aisling! Are you okay? You're going all red."

"Look, I'm twelve years old, okay? So I'm sure now you want to go off and find someone your own age because I'm sure you think I'm a baby!" I was practically in tears. Which made me feel like a total baby.

Actually, it turned out okay, because he still likes me, even though I'm a gigantic two years younger than him, and we watched a video together – Father Of The Bride, Part II. He suggested it when he saw it lying on top of the TV.

Naturally, it would have to be a comedy, but with some emotional bits, well, I think so anyway, and I always cry at films, no matter how funny they're supposed to be. (As you can imagine, I bawl my eyes out whenever a film is supposed to be sad.)

I caught him looking at me strangely. "I always cry at films," I informed him. "It's a profession. You can imagine what I was like at Titanic."

"As in, flooding in the cinema?"

"Precisely."

Sunday   *19th April*

I hate having a little brother. Henry is so annoying! I know all little brothers are but he really pushes the limit. He's even more annoying now that he has a Nintendo 64. He bored us enough for the six months before he got it, buying games before he could even play them, but now he's even worse, and he gets really frustrated and throws incredible temper tantrums where he goes crazy, stamping and kicking and crying and yelling and whacking his hand off his head. It's almost scary. He also pesters me constantly, and not, as my parents have idiotically suggested more than once, because he looks up to me, but because he loves annoying me. He insults me constantly, knowing exactly which buttons to push – he's been honing his insulting-Aisling skills for the past nine years. Whenever we're fighting, I always get blamed, just because I'm the oldest. That's absolutely ridiculous. When I was his age they were blaming me, saying I should have more cop-on. But apparently, now he's that age, he shouldn't, simply because of the totally unfair fact that he's the youngest. I hate it, I really do.

Monday   20th April

I've just finished my dinner and in a few minutes I have to rush. Amy's having a sort of party at her house, but not exactly. Conor and Orla were in a car crash over the weekend, and they're in hospital, so we're having a get-together at Amy's house to organise present-getting and see if anyone else has got any information.

Later   10:45

It was like a party, really. There were bottles of Cidona and Coke, bowls of crisps, chocolate, and penny-sweets. We made personalised get-well-soon cards on Amy's computer and printed them out in colour.

Kate and Trevor looked pretty depressed at the start, but Emma was acting like everything was okay. She always does that, adopts an air of nonchalance. Why can't she just show her emotions for once?

Friday   24th April

Kevin and I went to the Youth Club disco, as he's just joined. He asked me to go with him – and of course I said yes, do you think I'm stupid? We also got pretty intimate, meeting practically every second!

Saturday   25th April

A few of us went into the hospital to see Conor and Orla. Kate was a nervous wreck, so I went down with her to see Conor. He has a broken leg and has to stay in hospital for another week or two. Orla's getting out tomorrow, as she hit her head but is fine now.

Wednesday   29th April

Today was so chaotic. After our first fifteen-minute break, which ended at eleven, Alison and I went down to the assembly hall, where the auditions were going to be held. Mr Fitzsimons and Miss Devlin were there.

"Okay, girls, here's the plan," Miss Devlin said. "Aisling, you go into my room, number fifteen, and groups will be sent in to you. Teach them a song they'll need to know and if they can't sing that loud or that high or whatever, eliminate them. Send the remaining ones to Alison or Mr Fitzsimons, who will test their acting ability. Other times you might be sent smaller groups that have already been testing for their acting. Eliminate any that can't sing the songs."

We were given notebooks and pens, to make notes on the kids who were auditioning.

I was so busy from eleven-thirty until the end of school. My throat is killing me now, from singing so much.

Some of the groups were incredibly pathetic. I actually lost my temper – hear that, anyone who says I'm perfect? – with some of the groups.

At twelve-thirty, Alison and I were both exhausted, plus we both wanted to have our friends around, so we went up to Mr Fitzsimons to ask if we could get our friends to help us out a bit. He said yes, because he could see how tired we were, so Kate, Megan, and Amy, hung around for the rest of the day, helping out.

By the way, the three of them did great in both parts of the audition, and they each got the parts they wanted.

The rehearsing for the play won't start until the week after next, because next week, a crowd of us sixth class are going to the Gaeltacht in Donegal. And it's going to be absolutely GREAT!

Tuesday   5th May

So, here I am in Donegal, sharing a room with Alison, Megan, and Orla. We're having a great time, at least I am, anyway. The family we're with are really nice, and the food is gorgeous! Kate, Emma, Amy, and Helen are just in the next room, and we're allowed to stay up until ten o' clock, and of course we talk after Lights Out. I brought my pen that has a light at the end, so that it's sort of like a torch.

We're going to have a céilí most nights, and we've had

our first one. It was great fun. All the boys were messing around, of course, and when we did the dance where you spin around with your partner, it was crazy! I was dizzy after it.

The Irish classes are great fun. I expected them to be boring, but they're not! And I'm using a few sentences more than others – Rachfaidh mé dul go dtí an siopa agus ceannoidh mé milseáin being the main one!

I don't know if everyone's enjoying it as much as I am, though. Kate seems depressed, probably missing Conor. And I don't think everyone is enjoying the Irish classes and stuff. Maybe I should go and cheer up some people.

Thursday   7th May

Only two more days until my thirteenth birthday! I'd almost forgotten about it. I'm not having a sleepover – it'd be too boring after this week, so I'm not really doing anything.

Last night, no, wait, the night before, was great fun. Alison and I stayed up late, and I was telling her all about Kevin, and then Kate came in – she misses Conor. It's so cute the way her face lights up whenever she talks about him and that sappy smile she gets. But I probably look the same whenever I go on about Kevin.

Megan and Helen joined in next, and then everyone else came in, and we were chatting for a good two hours. I missed breakfast yesterday morning, I was so tired.

Saturday   9th May

So, here we are on the long coach ride back to Dublin. Helen and I are up in the front, because she gets carsick sometimes. The eight of us got to the coach late because we were messing around, so we're all sitting in different places.

The disco was last night. It was the usual – people messing around, others practically doing it on the dance floor and some of us sitting around talking.

I'm thirteen now – a teenager! Kate and Alison bought me some sweets when we stopped, and everyone else had forgotten.

Monday   11th May

I feel like I could just go to sleep and never wake up again. Unfortunately, I still have homework to do and Mum is nagging me to tidy my room. The reason I'm practically comatose is that after school we had a rehearsal that took two hours, plus I had to stay afterwards and help tidy up, so I didn't get home until after five.

All the people in our class who are involved in the play – a lot, if you count the people who are doing stuff like costumes and props – asked Mrs Lyons for homework off, but she said then we'd expect homework off every time we had a rehearsal, and we have rehearsals going on twice or three times a week until mid-June, so I can see her point. Still . . .

Yesterday I made out these little booklets, with the words and music of the songs, one made specially for everyone with major parts. Like Megan's has only the songs she sings and so on. Alison was dead impressed. So was everyone else, I think, so it was worth all the hard work.

It's great teaching everyone the songs that I wrote. Alan Young is playing the male lead and he has three or four songs. He's a good singer, and he can read music, so he's picked it up without getting me to sing any of them – which is a good thing because I can't sing that low! I had to play it all out on my keyboard to see if it sounded okay.

Kate, Amy and Megan are all great singers, as well as being good at acting, and they said – and I quote – "the songs are so cool!" (Megan), "deadly!" (Amy), and "wow, these songs sound so professional! And the lyrics are brilliant!" (Kate). I'm glad they like them. I put so much effort into them. I was sort of expecting to feel like when I put tons of effort into an essay and Mrs Lyons says it's rubbish. (Which happens a lot, now that I think about it. I hate it when she does that!)

Anyway, it took ages. Carol and Ann Hanley kept on whining. Unfortunately, they have major roles in the play – at least they don't have to sing, as they're both crows. Alan and Megan kept on messing around together. Mr Fitzsimons looked as if he was regretting choosing them for the parts, so I dragged Megan off to teach her Who Needs Boys, Anyway? Of course, when she came back out to sing it, Alan pretended to be all upset, and then of course he started on Give Me A Decent Girlfriend to retaliate. They're both songs that come after the break-up in the middle of the play.

Kate, Amy and Megan have to learn Your Friends Are

Always There For You which they sing together. That's near the end. We did that whole final scene, scripts in hand. After the song, Alan comes on, big apology scene, and Megan goes, "Of course, there's nothing wrong with having great friends and a boyfriend, is there?" Then Megan and Alan kiss (they like doing that scene!) and Amy and Kate pretend to gag behind them, and that's the end. I love it. If I was a better actress I'd have tried out, just to do that scene.

Thursday   *14th May*

We had another rehearsal today. We only have a month or so until we perform, so we're having tons of practices.

There's no more choir for this year, as Miss Devlin is doing the play and most the choir are involved in it. Anyway, there's nothing coming up that we need to sing at.

Today, I took Kate and Amy for the singing and they sang the ones that they'd learnt. Kate got really frustrated with one of the songs, and it didn't help that Amy is learning the songs no problem, so I suggested practising after the rehearsal. I went round to her house after dinner. Her mum is turning their house into a B&B, and there were people building an extension onto the back, and her mum was cleaning all the upstairs.

Kate has all her bedroom stuff moved into her sitting-room, so it's totally cool. She has her bed and wardrobe and locker at one end, the desk and couch in the middle, and then the TV, bookshelf, and her CD player at the other end. I'd love to have a room like that!

Anyway, we went over that song, I Hate Being Me, which inevitably makes me feel like I'm going to start crying, until she got it. It's a pretty difficult song, actually, to learn.

Thursday   21st May

A group of us were at Kate's house tonight. I was the only one there not part of a couple, but Kate and Conor were very thoughtfully including me in their conversations, so it was almost impossible not to feel left out.

Trevor got really upset, though, during the evening. His mum has an incurable form of cancer, and he was crying for loads of the time. I feel so sorry for him. I don't know how I'd cope if that was me. I just can't imagine any of my family ever dying. It's really scary, isn't it?

Later

You will not believe this. James and Amy are fighting, and naturally she's dead annoyed about it. She was even more annoyed a few minutes ago when I rang her and told her that James asked if I wanted to go with him again today! Obviously, I told him to get lost. At least Amy's not annoyed with me.

Friday   29th May

Okay, so I was wrong about Amy not being annoyed with me. At the disco tonight, after Kate and Conor had made up (don't get me started!) she ran out in tears, and when

I followed her, she got dead annoyed, saying James still liked me and he'd been staring at me . . .

It got awful. Finally we both just hugged silently, both of us crying. She said, sniffling, that she knew it wasn't really my fault. I still feel guilty, though. I can't help it.

Monday   1st June

James is a total moron. I mean, a few months ago he broke up with me so that he could go out with Amy, and today he broke it off with Amy because he likes me again. We both hate him now. The only fun time we had with him, we agree, is today – when they broke up and he looked over at me and I gave him my best icy glare, and then we both walked off on him. He looked so idiotic, and I didn't even feel sorry for him – so there!

Friday   5th June

Kevin and I went to see Sliding Doors at the UCI cinema in the Square tonight. It's 15s, so I put on some make-up, just a bit of eyeshadow and lipstick, to make myself look a bit older. It worked, whatever it was. I think it helped that lately I've grown an extra few inches. The film was brilliant. It's the one starring Gywenth Paltrow, the weird one where you see two parallel universes. I love the theme song, by Aqua. I was singing "If only I could turn back time . . ." all the way home.

Monday 8th June

We didn't have a rehearsal today, but a few of us – me, Alison, Megan, Kate, Amy, and Alan, we all stayed behind for a while, just to go over some of the stuff. It's in only sixteen days, our first performance, so we're all pretty nervous, even me and Alison, because what if the songs and the dialogue sound stupid?

Alison and I had to write a little bit for the programme. They're starting work on it now. I think Helen has volunteered to do some typing for it or something. We all had to get our photos taken for it as well, those passport-size photos. Well, most of us did. The minor characters will just be in the huge group photo that's going to be in the centre.

I'm sick of practising. I know most of Megan's lines, and when Kate did her part, I was mouthing along with her for the whole time. At least it means if one of them is sick there'll be no problem!

Tuesday 9th June

We had a practice today. I'm fed up of it. Megan and Amy looked fed up as well. The only one who looked remotely cheerful was Kate – because she was going home! I told her she might as well. She knows all her lines off by heart, anyway. When Megan wanted to practise the scene where she and Kate fight, I practised it with her. Megan said afterwards that I was performing exactly like Kate, with the same movements and gestures. I suppose it's that I've

44

watched them doing this scene so many times. And in the next scene, there's a solo for Kate, which I absolutely love. I swear, anytime Carol is around while Kate is singing that, she starts crying. It's I Hate Being Me, and it's just so depressing and yet beautiful at the same time. It's so hard to believe I actually wrote it, that I created the lyrics and the music, that it can affect Carol and the rest of them so much.

Saturday   13th June

For mid-June, the weather has been pretty awful lately. It was raining on Thursday, which was the day of our school tour. But it was to Blessington, and we were on the lake for half the day anyway, so it didn't really matter. I was in a group with Emma, Amy, Conor, Brian and James. It was a bit awkward for James, I noticed, at the start. Well, obviously it would be, on a team with three of his ex-girlfriends. Yes, three, he and Emma were going together in fifth class, I think. We must all compare notes sometime. Anyway, we were all dead casual and friendly after a while.

We did windsurfing first. There was no point, really, you can't learn much in an hour and a quarter, so we just messed around. Amy and I were on a board together, and Emma and Conor were, and Brian and James were, and the instructor went crazy more than once – we were messing around so much! Normally I wouldn't, it's not fair to everyone who wants to learn, but we were the only ones with that instructor, and we were all messing. I pushed James off his board and he came up dripping wet and annoyed. "Bitch," he muttered and pulled me in, and I grabbed on to him so that he'd fall in again. We were still clutching each other when we resurfaced, and we were laughing. For a moment it felt like we were going together again, we felt so comfortable around each other. And I feel like such a slapper, and I don't think I could ever tell anyone this, but . . . I wanted to kiss him just then. Me! If any of my friends found out they'd be shocked.

"Feeling sexy?" he asked mischievously, with that adorable cocky grin on his face. Thankfully, I recovered in time. "In your dreams," I said sweetly, and pulled myself up on the surfboard.

I went over to Kevin's as soon as I came home to remind myself that he's my boyfriend. But last night I had a weird dream. We were all much older, and I was married to Kevin, and then I ran into James again, and was torn between the two. Finally I went back to Kevin. That was when I woke up. Hey! That's what happened in Casablanca! I need to get a life!

Monday   15th June

Okay, forget all about James. He was a pain in the you-know-what today. He's so much nicer in my daydreams. Oh, well, c'est la vie, as the song goes.

Thursday   25th June

I barely have enough energy to write. I'm more tired than I ever have been in my life. The first performance of the play was on last night. After soothing many nerves – Kate was really upset, in tears, and Amy was chewing her nails so much I'm surprised she didn't choke. Alan was wrecked. He couldn't even crack a joke. He was just stunned. Considering that, it's a miracle the first performance went terrifically.

The second one, tonight, went just as well. There were just as many people there and no one was nervous this time. I did the make-up for both nights. That's me – composer, music director, make-up artist. With all the experience I've accumulated I could make a fortune in Hollywood!

Saturday   27th June

The disco last night went brilliantly. I kissed Brian! I couldn't help it, he looked so depressed watching Carol having fun, so I impulsively asked him to dance. (Yes, I asked him. Haven't you ever heard of equality?) I know I'm going with Kevin, so I felt really guilty afterwards, but then I told Kevin about it, and he said it was fine with him. He thinks I meant a friendly peck. I chose not to correct him. I felt like a slapper, but I got over it. I deserve to have some fun once in a while!

Speaking of fun . . . I love acting! Kate showed up today early with a sore throat and everyone went into a panic. Alison and Kate both said I could do it, so I finally agreed. I almost forgot a few lines, but not quite. It was fun, actually, when I wasn't nervous. And singing my songs for everyone felt wonderful.

Tuesday   *30th June*

I'm going to miss everyone so much! I didn't realise how close I'd gotten to some people this year. I've sort of drifted away from Alison and more towards Kate. And Megan and Amy. I'm going to miss everyone, though. I hope we'll all stay friends, but it seems doubtful. I feel like freezing at this point in time and staying here permanently. But since I can't do that, I suppose I'm going to have to "go with the flow". I know I'll miss being in primary school with everyone, but you always have memories, right? And, you know, it's kind of exciting, when you think about it. Starting a new school, almost a new life. . . . Still, I'll never forget certain things – the skiing trip – (I hated that!), the Gaeltacht trip, the play. (Mostly) terrific memories of times that me and my friends shared, times that I know I'll never forget.

2:   Alison's Diary

Fact-File

Name:: Alison Taylor

Age:: 12, will be 13 on March 6th

Family:: Parents divorced, lives with mum, only child

Looks:: Light brown hair down to shoulders, greenish-bluish eyes

Hobbies:: reading, writing stories, hanging around with her friends

Ambitions:: to be a writer – preferably famous!

School:: Hillside Primary, will be going into Loreto Secondary

Friends:: Aisling, Amy, Megan, Emma

Worst Enemies:: Donna Jones and co.

Favourite T.V. programmes:: Mad About You, Friends, Veronica's Closet

Favourite Actors:: Leonardo DiCaprio, Matthew Perry

Favourite Actresses:: Lisa Kudrow, Helen Hunt, Kate Winslet, Kirstie Alley

Favourite Films:: Titanic, Gone With The Wind, An Affair To Remember

Favourite Books:: Sisters . . . No Way!, Kirsten, Different Lives, Pillars of Fire

Favourite Authors:: Siobhán Parkinson, Elspeth Cameron, Jane Mitchell

Claire Hennessy

Favourite Singers:: Louise, Celine Dion, Mariah Carey, Toni Braxton

Favourite Groups:: Eternal, All Saints, Carter Twins, Backstreet Boys

Favourite Song:: Always Be My Baby by Mariah Carey

Favourite Album:: Woman In Me by Louise

Tuesday   10/2/98

We're all planning to go up to the Square next Monday to
see Titanic. It's supposed to be great. Although Leonardo
DiCaprio is gorgeous and a great actor, Kate Winslet is
supposed to steal the show.

Mum came in today all happy and cheerful. It must be
her new boyfriend. His name's Chris, she tells me, and he
works with her. He's the first boyfriend she's had since she
and Dad split up, and that was years ago.

Thursday   12/2/98

Mrs Lyons was in a really grouchy mood today. She was
out yesterday, sick, so maybe that was why. Anyway, just
because Aisling didn't read a chapter of the book that we're
reading that she could have easily read during break time,
Mrs Lyons really lost it, and started yelling at her, about
being responsible and how "whatever secondary school
you're going to, young lady, will not tolerate that type of
behaviour and neither will I!". It was absolutely awful, and
Mrs Lyons blew it totally out of proportion. The whole
class was trying to look like we were doing our work, because
we were terrified of being the next one she'd pick on.

She actually had Aisling crying over it all through break
time, and as if that wasn't enough humiliation for Ash, then
Amy and Emma started going on about how it just wasn't
"socially acceptable for anyone in sixth class to be crying in
front of the class". Isn't that horrible? So now Megan, Aisling
and I aren't speaking to them, for obvious reasons.

Saturday   *14/2/98*

I found out today that Mum's boyfriend is Megan's dad! Isn't that unbelievable? Megan and I were laughing about it.

Emma and Amy apologised, so now we're all talking. (Aww, group hug!) We all had a good time at the Valentine's Disco last night. Aisling found herself a boyfriend there, James Robinson, who's in our class.

The rest of us stood in the corner, gossiping, and observing. We didn't actually mind too much no one asked us to dance. Okay, so I did, but I pretended I didn't. I do that a lot. I've only been to about three discos in my life, and never been asked to dance – well, seriously anyway.

Monday   *16/2/98*

Unbelievable. Absolutely unbelievable. Mum has paid for me to go on the skiing trip! She told me last night. It's sort of a birthday present, as my 13th birthday is on the day after we come back. This is fantastic! The trip to Italy is THE trip of the year, and it's only for sixth class. Aisling, Megan and Emma are going, as well as a few others from our class. It's going to be great! I can't ski at all, but I hope I'll pick it up fast!

I can remember being in school around this time of the year for the past few years, and the sixth class would be boasting about the ski trip. I've always wanted to go – and now I can!

Tuesday   17/2/98

Titanic was brilliant. I loved it. You should've seen me during the sad bits, I was bawling! And Aisling, beside me, was crying so hard she was shaking. The film was great, really. Whenever Leonardo DiCaprio was on the screen, our eyes were glued to it!

Saturday   21/2/98

Megan's slumber party, for her twelfth birthday, was terrific. We watched three films, talked all night, did each other's nails and hair, ate tons of sweets, and had tons of fun. Megan did her impressions of people, which had us in bits, and Amy did really artistic things with our nails. I mean it, she's very artistic, and you can tell just by looking at her nails. She always does something with them, even though nail varnish isn't allowed in our school. Last night she painted half them purple glitter, the other half pink with silver glitter, and she put nail transfers over that. It looked great.

What else? Oh, yeah, Aisling sang some of those songs Phoebe sings in Friends, and we all cracked up. She knows them all off by heart, naturally. And we all joined in for "Smelly Cat".

Friday   27/2/98

After arriving in Milan Airport yesterday we went by coach to the ski resort. It's quite nice, and there are a few other school groups here. And a few of the staff speak English, thank God! Our room is lovely – huge, with the beds spaced out, and a desk, two wardrobes, and an en suite bathroom. Naturally, Megan, Aisling, Emma and I are sharing the room. Across the hall, there are Orla and Carol, two others from our class, and down the hall a bit, a few of the boys.

The skiing today went okay. Emma's been skiing before and Megan's a natural at it, so they went up the higher group. I'm okay at it and Aisling is pathetic, so we're still in the beginners group, but it's still fun.

Aisling got really upset after dinner – it was either the gross octopus or the fact she was absolutely hopeless at skiing. She rushed up to our room in tears, and I followed her up to comfort her.

I feel sorry for her, because it really matters to her whether she's good at skiing or not. But she should realise that she doesn't have to be good at everything she tries. I mean, she's smart, and a brilliant singer and musician. There's only so much you can do, you know?

Megan's preoccupied with boys at the moment – specifically, self-proclaimed class clown-cum-psycho Alan Young. Then there's Emma, all she cares about is the skiing. They haven't even noticed how miserable Aisling is.

Saturday   28/2/98

There was an accident on the ski slopes today. Someone swerved into Orla's path, so she swerved to avoid them and crashed right into Emma. Emma broke her left arm and Orla has a twisted ankle, so neither of them can ski.

Sunday   1/3/98

I'm getting better at skiing. Today I was put into the higher group. It was really fun. I surprised myself by being able to do all the stuff we had to do.

Aisling didn't go skiing today, and Emma didn't either, naturally, so I suppose they must have gone into the games room or viewing-room. Or maybe the children's lounge.

I wish I had a laptop computer, because I have all these great ideas for stories and I'm used to writing them on the computer at home. I hate writing them out on paper, because if I make a mistake I have to start all over again.

Monday   2/3/98

Today was the designated shopping day. About thirty of the forty kids who are on the tour came shopping, the rest chose to stay and ski, and they can get stuff in the Duty Free at the airport on Thursday.

We were split up into groups, with a teacher supervising each group. Me, Aisling, Emma, Megan, and Orla were all sitting in the back seat of the coach that brought us into Milan to shop, so we formed one group. Mrs Lyons supervised. We thought she was going to be really strict but she was actually really nice.

We had such a great time. We were all laughing, and Megan was doing impressions, and then she and Aisling went into their Phoebe routine – first "Smelly Cat" and then the Christmas one, and so on.

It's weird shopping in Italy. Everything seems to cost so

much, but it's just that it's something like two or three thousand lira to equal a pound, so you can see how that turns out!

I bought chocolates for Mum, and I bought Amy a few things – a plastic pasta keyring, a big bar of Italian dark chocolate, and a necklace with European flags hanging from the silver beads. I feel sort of guilty about being here having fun while Amy's in school, working, especially since I didn't think I was going on the trip, so the two of us had lots of things planned together.

Tuesday   3/3/98

We finally convinced Aisling to come skiing with us today, but when we were going up in the cable car she suddenly got really scared and upset. She had to take the cable car down as well.

I felt so guilty over not going back down with her, but Megan told me not to worry and that I was getting way too sensitive for my own good. I laughed when she said that, because that's what I say to Aisling all the time!

Going home is going to be great, even though I'm enjoying myself here. I can't wait to find out how Amy got on. I just hope she isn't having a miserable time. Hey, what am I saying? Amy could take the Great Famine and make it into the most enjoyable thing on earth.

Wednesday 4/3/98

Aisling claimed she was "sick" this morning. I was talking to her this evening, though, and she confessed she was faking because she's so scared of going up and skiing down a mountain. I feel sorry for her – which I've been doing a lot of, I know! But it's not like it's much fun coming on a skiing trip and then being too scared to enjoy yourself, is it? Just like it's not much fun coming and then breaking your arm. (Especially when it's your left arm so that when you get back to school you still have to write.)

Thursday 5/3/98

We've just got onto the plane. Aisling is beside me and Megan, Orla and Emma are behind me. I have my Discman with me, plus a book to read and a packet of mints to suck on. I'm reading this deadly new book by Jane Mitchell, the one who wrote "When Stars Stop Spinning" – we read that in school this year – and "Different Lives", which is one of my favourite books ever. So far this one – it's called "Making Waves" – is turning out to be just as good, if not better. I bought about five new books to read on this trip, expecting I'd have lots of free time, but it didn't turn out that way – we were busy for most of the day and at night we were exhausted.

Two and a quarter hours until we're back in Ireland. I can't wait.

The holiday is over

The journey home has begun
Mixed feelings envelope me
I want to be home once more
But I still wish the holiday didn't have to end.

We're flying over the Alps now. It's an incredible view. I wish I had my camera, but it's with my luggage.

The majestic Alps are beneath me
Snow covering each and every peak
It's like a beautiful painting
That I'll want to look at again
But I can't.
I must savour the moment
Before it's too late
I must admire the beauty
Of the majestic Alps.

Later

Amy came to the airport to see us! She came with Emma's mum and was really happy to see us all.

Back home with my mum
Back home with my friends
In my own room
In my own house
In my own estate
In my own country
Where I belong.
It's good to be home.

Saturday   7/3/98

Well, it's official – I'm a teenager! I got some great presents at my slumber party last night, including the Titanic soundtrack.

Tuesday   10/3/98

HOLD EVERYTHING! At a school assembly today the teachers were telling us about the school play they hope to put on in June. They need someone to write it, and they want a student to write it! It has to be written by the end of March. During the whole time the teachers were talking about it, Megan was looking at me as if she was saying, Earth to Alison! Wake up, Al! You could write the play!

It's a crazy idea, of course. The Confirmation is on soon, and there's really no time for anyone to come up with a good idea for a play and write it in just three weeks!

Except . . . I could use the idea from one of my stories and turn it into a play! Let's see, I could use the one about the girl called Samantha. I think I'll call it Thirteen.

THIRTEEN: SCENE ONE
In a classroom

Samantha: Okay, hands up anyone who's a psycho!
    (Looks expectantly at Helen)
Helen (lifting hand): Me! I'm a certified psycho!
Liz: Tell us something we don't know!
Samantha (laughs): Hey, Helen, feel like coming over
    to my house tonight? Your dad and my mum are

going out for another "romantic dinner". (Pretends to gag.)

Helen: Another one? Shoot me!

Liz: Huh! At least your dad isn't going out with a nineteen-year-old!

Mum's just called me for dinner. Gotta go!

Later

I'm going to have to make some changes to my story, because I know the teachers will want to involve as many people as possible. I'll write some scenes which involve younger kids. And I think I should have songs and music in it. Only problem is, I want original songs in it. It'll make it way better. But I can't write music, even if I might be able to write lyrics. I'm going to ask Aisling about it.

Wednesday   *11/3/98*

Mum and Chris are ENGAGED! They plan on getting married in September and Mum and I will be moving in with Megan and Chris over the summer.

Megan and I are going to be stepsisters! I can't wait!

Thursday   *12/3/98*

SCENE FIVE
In the kitchen of the Murphys' house, where Liz and Sam are baby-sitting

Samantha: Liz, don't lie to me. I heard you throwing up in there! What's up?

Liz: Nothing! Absolutely nothing!

Samantha: Come on, Liz. I know when something's up.

Liz: Oh, just shut up, Sam. Stop thinking you're always right and everyone else is always wrong. I told you, nothing's wrong.

Samantha: Except that you're throwing up! What is it, Liz? Are you sick or – oh, no. This has something to do with those idiots who said you were fat, doesn't it?

Liz: This has nothing to do with them! If I think I need to lose a little weight –

Samantha: If you lose "a little weight" you'll be a toothpick! You're bulimic, Liz, aren't you?

Liz: No! (starts yelling) Now get lost! I never want to talk to you again!

Friday   *13/3/98*

It's official – I'm writing the school play. We had an assembly today, just for fifth and sixth class, and everyone who had an idea for the play and who were willing to work on it had to talk about their ideas. I was so nervous when I looked up and saw two hundred and forty kids staring at me! But the vote was practically unanimous – I'm writing the play!

There's still the music, though. Aisling is going to ask

the choir teacher for a bit of help, but otherwise she thinks she can do it.

Monday   16/3/98

My Confirmation was today. I don't feel any different – or maybe I do. Oh, I don't know.

Aisling has spoken to Miss Devlin, and now Aisling is going to start working on music and lyrics. I've told her what the play's about so that she'll know what sort of stuff to write.

I've been reading up on bulimia, just to make sure all the facts in my play are correct. Did you know that boys can suffer from eating disorders as well? I didn't, you always think It's a girls' thing.

Wednesday   18/3/98

Aisling and I are working really hard on the play. We haven't got much longer to finish it. It's due by the end of March, as the teachers want to look over it during the Easter holidays. Aisling has already written some great songs, and she's sung them for me to see if they're appropriate. Megan is helping us out as well. She acts some of the scenes out and puts on different voices so that I can see if they work out okay or not.

SCENE ELEVEN

In the classroom

Helen is sitting in the centre of a group of kids.

Helen: Honestly! Samantha can really be bossy! I mean, last night, she kept on nagging at me to tidy my room! She sounded as bad as her mum!

(Samantha walks in silently. No-one notices.)

Helen: Then she started on, (in prissy, high voice) "Shouldn't you be doing your homework? Shouldn't you be working on your project?"

Samantha: How about, shouldn't you be loyal to your friends?

(Everyone turns around and looks at her in shock.)

Samantha: And, by the way, I was just saying all that stuff because I wanted you to get lost. But you just can't take a hint, can you? You're so thick.

(Turns and walks out)

Friday   *20/3/98*

I can't believe how much attention Aisling and I are getting because of the play! Today, in yard, everyone was crowding around us, bombarding us with questions. It was amazing!

Wednesday   *25/3/98*

I still have another bit to do on the play. I have a regular routine. As soon as I come home from school I rush through my homework and then get to work on the play.

I wasn't able to work on it today, because Mum was using the computer all afternoon for something for her work. So I was waiting around impatiently and we ended up having a fight.

Monday   30/3/98

I had a fight with Amy as well. No one understands how important this play is, they don't take me seriously when I say I need to work on it! They expect me to drop everything to be with them and mess around. My friends can be so immature.

I finally handed in the play today, after working on it non-stop all weekend.

Thursday   2/4/98

The Easter holidays start tomorrow. I'll be glad of the break. As soon as we're back, the auditions for the play will begin. Aisling and I will be assisting the teachers in choosing the actors. Aisling's also going to be teaching them the songs, as she's the only one who knows them.

Amy and I are talking to each other now. On Tuesday we both came in, said "hi" to each other and that was it.

Mum is acting all dreamy and ditzy now. I'm serious. It's like living in Friends. With Phoebe. It has to be Chris. I must ask Megan if he's acting weird too. If he is, we can get together for a moan-about-parents session.

Speaking of Megan, she's been acting really weird lately. Maybe she's feeling weird about the soon-to-be marriage.

Or maybe it's the entrance exam we have coming up in a few weeks.

Saturday   4/4/98

You won't believe what I heard Mum and Chris talking about. Megan is in Paris right now, I found out, which is why none of us have been able to contact her. She's visiting her mother. This is what I've put together: Megan's mother left eight years ago, to go to Paris, and Megan feels awful about that. Her mum hasn't contacted her in ages. She's a terrific actress, who's worked in plays and films. Poor Megan! What a situation! Her mum is doing what Megan would love to be doing, acting and living in Paris. But Megan must be feeling confused because in order to live like this, her mum had to leave her. I'll talk to her when she gets back.

Wednesday   8/4/98

Well, I'm bored, and it's only a few days into the holidays. I don't feel like writing stories, or reading, or watching TV. I can't do anything about Megan, and I don't have any Easter eggs to eat. I'm glad I signed up for the Easter camp in the school next week, at least that will be something to do. All my friends are going, and there'll be lots of different activities to do. The best part is, we won't have to do anything we don't like, as we get to sign up for whatever activities we like best. They have creative writing – great! – and drama, music, arts and crafts, as well as sports. There's also a table quiz on the last day and swimming on the second day.

Friday   10/4/98

Megan's coming home tomorrow. She probably won't want to talk to us, but she's going to the camp so we'll see her on Tuesday.

Saturday   11/4/98

I wonder if I'll ever get a boyfriend. As unbelievable as it sounds, I've never gone with anyone before. And it really makes me wonder. I consider myself mature, certainly as mature as the rest of my friends, so why don't I have a boyfriend?

While we're on the "mature" thing, why haven't I got my period, either? Amy and Aisling have, and they're younger than me! Life's not fair.

Tuesday   14/4/98

Nineteen Easter eggs. Amazing. Nineteen Easter eggs is what I got, and I've eaten eight of them already.

At the Easter camp today, I did creative writing, arts and crafts, basketball, tennis, and I skipped the last hour-long session. I hid out in one of the classrooms, one far away from everything, and I read this book I bought yesterday, Forever by Judy Blume.

Megan 'fessed up about her mum, and turns out she and

her mum get along great now, so basically I've been worrying for the last while all for nothing. Typical.

Wednesday   15/4/98

We went swimming today. It was brilliant. I'm usually hopeless at anything remotely sporty, but I'm a great swimmer, if I do say so myself. And just did.

Thursday   16/4/98

We had a treasure hunt today, at least all of us in the "A" group, which is everyone who came from sixth class. We were put into teams of four, and I was with Amy, Helen, and Carol. It's sickening the way Carol bosses Helen around, or at least tries to, but Helen stuck up for herself a lot today. I was surprised.

It was kind of awkward with the four of us on one team, because I barely know Helen or Carol, but Amy and Helen are good friends, so they were yapping away. Note, Helen can actually talk normally, instead of in that quiet voice she uses in school.

We were trying to beat the team with Aisling, Emma, Kate, Orla and Megan on it. Lucky them, they were the last group, so there was one left over. They beat us, unfortunately. With three ultra-sporty girls to run around getting the clues, no wonder.

Friday   *17/4/98*

Kate came over this evening. We have this project to do
for school, and we have to do it together. It's due in a few
weeks, but we both wanted to get it over with, because
auditions for the play start almost as soon as we get back,
and I'll be doing a lot with them, and Kate's planning to
try out.

Anyway, she was over for about four hours, and we were
exhausted at the end of it, but at least we'd done half our
project. We were sprawled out on the sitting-room floor
and we got talking about the kids in our class.

"Conor's really nice," she sighed, "and I know you're not
going to believe this, but he's so sensitive."

"Conor?" I said. Conor always acts macho. I was
extremely sceptical.

"I mean it. He is so nice. And supportive. And
gorgeous . . ."

"You're so lucky."

"That's what Aisling told me."

"Aisling?"

"Yeah. She's really nice, isn't she?"

"Yeah, she is. I mean, really nice."

"Like supportive."

"Exactly. And really fair, and thoughtful, you know?"

"The sort of person you imagine yourself being, but you
really know you could never be like that?"

I nodded. "Speaking of thoughtful – that's exactly what
you're being right now. I never thought of you as that
type."

She looked me straight in the eye. "What type do you see me as?" she asked bluntly.

"You know, one of the cool girls, really sporty."

"With no feelings."

"No! Not like that!" But I realised then, that that was how I thought of her. Which made me wonder. I mean, I think I'm so fair and unbiased and everything. But it turns out I'm not, really. I'm not perfect. No one is, and I guess I'm just really starting to acknowledge that. Which makes me jealous of Aisling, because she really does seem perfect.

"That's what I mean," Kate sighed then. "Practically everyone in our class has this image they project of themselves, so that they can act like they're cool and as if nothing bothers them."

She has a point. She really does. She's not being thoughtful, well, she is, but there's some other word for it as well. Philosophical, that's what it is.

Monday   20/4/98

You won't believe what happened on Saturday. We found out about it today from Carol, otherwise known as The Gossip Queen. On Saturday, Conor's dad was driving Orla and Conor into town for something, and on the way, another car was out of control and crashed into them. Orla and Conor are in hospital now, but Carol doesn't know how badly injured they are. Oh God, this is awful.

Wednesday 29/4/98

I feel like I'm about to collapse at any minute. I didn't realise how much work I was volunteering to do when I agreed to write the play. Today Aisling and I had to go to the auditions and take groups of kids who were trying out, and then eliminating the hopeless ones.

It was exhausting. We were there from eleven until two-thirty. At around half-twelve we recruited Amy, Megan and Kate, who had just finished their auditions, to help us.

I was busy all the time. I had to deal with the groups of kids who were auditioning for all the major roles, and some of them were really pathetic. At two o' clock, the seven of us – me, Aisling, Kate, Megan, Amy, Miss Devlin and Mr Fitzsimons – all sat down together and made up the list. Kate, Megan and Amy all got the parts they wanted, by the way.

We found out that Orla and Conor are both going to be fine. Thank God.

Friday 1/5/98

Mum is absolutely crazy. Remember how I said it was like living with Phoebe from Friends? Well, It's worse. She forgot to make dinner so we had to go to McDonald's. Which is weird, because Mum never goes to any of those fast-food places, she's into really healthy food. She doesn't mind me going in there with my friends, but if I'm with her we never go in.

Mum also forgot to remind me to hoover my room, which

she always does on Fridays when she comes home from work. Not that I minded that. Oh, and she told me three times to remember to pack my navy jeans for the Gaeltacht. This is completely weird.

Thursday   7/5/98

It feels like we're much older, sixteen or seventeen, visiting Paris or London or someplace, staying in a youth hostel, going down to the shops or the chipper practically whenever we want, getting a video out (we did that tonight), being able to talk to each other late at night.

Saturday   9/5/98

We're on the coach travelling back to Dublin. The trip was great. We had a few céilís during the week, and a disco last night. The Irish classes went pretty well, very informal and good fun. And the family we were staying with, very friendly but kept their distance, and spoke that awful, ununderstandable Donegal Irish the whole time. Luckily, in the Irish college, there were lots of teachers from all around the country, so they spoke the normal Irish, if you can call it that.

What was great, though, was that the eight of us girls from the class – me, Aisling, Amy, Emma, Megan, Orla, Kate and Helen – were the only ones in the house, and our rooms were right next to each other, so we were constantly going in to see each other. One night, Wednesday, I think, we stayed up most of the night talking, with Aisling,

Amy, Megan, Kate and Helen yapping on about their "wonderful", "gorgeous", "amazing", "sensitive" boyfriends. Personally, I don't know how they can fancy any of the boys in our class. I mean, James is pretty thick. Alan is a total weirdo. Conor is so condescending and rude – well, in school, anyway. And Trevor is such a wimp! Either they turn into super-heroes after school or else it's true: love really is blind.

I feel like I've sort of misjudged my friends, though, because I always thought that most of my friends were . . . well, you know, not serious about anything really important, all they cared about was boys and clothes and TV programmes. They don't, really. And you know what else? I always thought that when you were our age, it was all crushes and "liking" boys, and when Kate or Helen or Aisling would say they were "in love", that they didn't really mean it, that they were just saying it, what they really meant was that they fancied someone. I think I might have been wrong about that. I mean, Kate talking about Conor, describing how sensitive he can be . . . (I know, it sounds ridiculous, in school he's such a pain). It's obvious that she really loves him, though. And Helen on Trevor. She confessed that she really loved it when he started crying at Titanic, because she said it showed that he had a sensitive side . . . (or else he's just a wimp).

We had a lot of fights, though, this week. I think we'd rather forget about them, though. Being together with all your friends is great for a while, but then they start getting on your nerves.

Another thing. I always thought no one really liked me,

72

except for Aisling and Megan, but this week has shown me that I was wrong. I've had a great time, with the girls and the boys.

Sunday 10/5/98

I am such an idiot, I don't know why I didn't see it sooner. Mum's pregnant! She invited Chris and Megan around and told us all together. The baby's due in six months, apparently. Imagine, my mother – my forty-one-year-old mother – is pregnant!

Chris got this big sappy look on his face, and Megan and I exchanged wow looks. Oh, it's going to be great, having a baby around. I'm going to have a little brother or sister – although I hope a sister – around. Well, a half-sister or brother, actually. I can't wait!

Tuesday 12/5/98

Today was a bit of a disaster. Amy and Emma are having a fight. I'm not sure how it started., but it got worse during first break, when we had to stay in because the yard was wet from all the rain this morning. Amy, as you know, is great at drawing, and even during maths or something she'll be doodling. Anyway, she drew a picture of a dog and turned over to show it to James, who sits behind her. The rest of us, except Emma, were over by the window.

"Emma," Amy grinned, pointing to the drawing, and Emma heard and she grabbed the drawing off her. She said she was going to tell Mrs Lyons after break. Amy got all worried then, and she started crying. We all went over to see what was wrong, and lots of people were already there, like James and Trevor and Conor, asking her very gently what was wrong, which sort of surprised me, because they were being really sensitive. I never thought they could actually be sensitive! (So I suppose Kate and Helen were right after all).

Anyway, we were all crowding around her, about ten of us, with Emma off to the side, sulking that Amy was getting all the attention, probably. Amy finally told us, and she was worrying for the rest of break. As soon as Mrs Lyons came in, she told us to go outside for a run around the yard – it really wasn't that wet – and me and Helen and Aisling were all jogging along with her at the same speed, reassuring her. Megan, Kate, and Orla were inside with Emma, who'd gone into the toilet.

The six of us are all trying to stay neutral, being nice to both of them, because we don't really want to take sides. Of course, Megan and Amy are really good friends, and so are Kate and Orla and Emma, so It's kind of hard.

Friday   15/5/98

Well, it turns out Amy and Emma made up – thank God! It was all a bit over the top, if you ask me. I'm glad they've cut it out.

We're still finding the play exhausting. Me and Aisling were talking about that today, actually. She has a sore throat all the time, because she has to teach all the main cast members the songs.

Today really felt like the start of summer. It was roasting hot, and no ne wore in a jacket or coat. And walking home, with the newly cut grass and the perfect blue sky and the hot sun . . . I can't wait for the summer holidays!

> Summer's Here
> Finally, summer's here
> It's nearly the end of the school year
> The sun is shining, bright and high
> In the perfect, blue, cloudless sky.
> The smell of newly cut grass
> As I stroll down the path
> It feels so great
> I just can't wait
> Until the holidays are here!

Monday 18/5/98

Megan, Chris, Mum, and I all went out last night and came back late, so naturally, this morning, Megan and I overslept. She called for me at about ten to nine, and as she rang the doorbell I was putting on my bra (yes, I do wear one, even though I barely need it, and I suppose you could call it a training bra, since it's one of those ones with ages and not bust sizes on it). Anyway, we ran all the way up to school, giggling hysterically, and when we reached the school it was five past nine, fifteen minutes after school started. Mrs Lyons gave out to us, but who cares? There's only another six or seven weeks left of school anyway. No one really bothers anymore. Everyone's coming in with their tracksuit on whenever they feel like it, and not doing all their home-work . . . at least Mrs Lyons isn't giving us as much homework as she used to, she must be getting into the summer spirit too.

Wednesday 20/5/98

The main topic of conversation now, besides holidays, is the disco. We're discussing what to wear to it and anyone who's on the committee is worrying about the DJ and the lights and the refreshments.

I have nothing to wear to it. I mean it – nothing. Zilch. No rip-offs, no flares, no hipsters, no combats (what are combats, anyway?).

No wonder none of the boys in the class will ever look at me! It is so depressing. I feel so ugly and fat, with my gross mousy brown hair and my eyes that simply can't decide which colour they want to be – they're sort of green and blue at the same time.

I wonder if I'm going to get my period soon. When we were at the Gaeltacht, that was one of the things we dis-cussed. Amy, Kate, Aisling all have. At least, they were the only ones who said they had. Some refused to say – like Megan, so she might or might not. Anyway, the point is, obviously It's not so unusual to get it when you're twelve or thirteen, as at least three out of eight of us have already, so why shouldn't I?

Monday   25/5/98

I've been thinking. Slang is so weird, isn't it? I mean, meeting means French kissing. And I know that the technical definition of frigid is a woman who doesn't enjoy sex, but in slang it means a girl who hasn't met someone. And a paedophile means someone who sexually abuses children, but used in slang it means you're going with someone too young. Very weird.

Tuesday   26/5/98

Some people in our class were talking about playing Spin The Bottle someday. They decided to drop it, but it got me thinking. It would sort of ruin your first kiss, wouldn't it? I mean, meeting someone you might not even like. Of course, all my friends don't have that problem – not even Helen! They've all gone off and left me behind these past few months – well, except for Emma, who's been meeting boys since fourth class. I sort of felt like I was much older, like eighteen, and the only virgin. It felt like that, really!

Wednesday   3/6/98

Oh yeah, I got that weird feeling again today. Emma and I are sitting near Carol and Brian, and don't get me started on the Robbie-Carol-Brian love triangle, it's far too complicated. Anyway, it felt so . . . you know, like something out of a soap or something (and I do watch Coronation Street, I know what I'm talking about). It's making me wish I had a boyfriend so badly, or at least that someone would ask me out – in my entire life, I've never been asked out. It's so depressing. Especially since everyone seems to have got their first kiss, and I'm left on my own, and it's so annoying with all the happy couples around – Kate and Conor, especially. At least they're really serious, I mean, I can see them staying together for ages, they're so comfortable together and they're friends, you know, as well as going together.

This is so depressing. I think maybe I'll just go watch TV.

Later

It was depressing, thought Jenny, that no-one ever asked her out. You'd think someone would. Thirteen and her world was falling apart, and all because none of the immature, annoying boys in her class liked her. It was absurd, but she couldn't help her feelings. Damn teenage hormones!

That just occurred to me. I'm a teenager, and I never really thought of it that way before. I've always thought of thirteen as a kind of pre-teen age, but still, I'm an actual teenager. It sounds weird, when I'm writing it, but it only actually struck me now. Funny, isn't it?

Friday   5/6/98

The play is on in two and a half weeks and some people still don't know their lines! At least my friends know most of theirs, because if they didn't I'm sure I'd be fighting with them. I didn't realise how hard this was going to be.

We have our first performance on Wednesday night, the

24th of June, and then another one on Thursday night, one on Friday afternoon (the disco is on Friday night, so Mr Fitzsimons wisely decided not to have a performance then) and our final performance on Saturday night. The reason we have to have so many is because we've been asking about all the meetings that are on for all the local clubs and groups and committees, to make sure our performances don't clash with any important meetings, and eventually we just decided to do the play four times.

Aisling and I had to write a piece for the play programme! We're both going to have our photographs and our pieces in it, near the start, and it's going to be so embarrassing! But, as the teachers keep saying, we did put so much work and effort into it, we deserve the credit. I agree with that – in principle, at least, but it's different when it actually happens. And naturally you have to write something nice about it, you can't exactly say, "There were times – a lot of them – when I wanted to give up, when I was totally fed up with it, when I wished I'd never written it", now, can you? You have to write something sappy like "I know I'll look back on this as one of the best times of my life. It was a thoroughly enjoyable experience". (Yeah, we both said stuff like that!)

Monday   8/6/98

Mum is starting to look pregnant. She's four months pregnant already, and she has all the basic symptoms. A textbook pregnancy. I hope everything goes okay, I mean, she is a bit on the old side for another kid. Technically, some of my friends could get pregnant! Technically, but I know they wouldn't do anything so stupid.

I hope it's a girl. I really do, I want to have a little sister. By the time she's my age, I'll be twenty-six and I'll be her cool half-sister. And then there's Madeleine's baby. She asked me to call her that the last time she phoned here, by the way. She also asked how the play rehearsals were going, and did I feel everything I'd written was going to turn out okay? Megan must have told her everything. She's really nice, actually. She'll be living here soon, in Dublin at least, if not in Hillside. She wants Megan to able to visit her easily.

As it turns out, actually, Mum and Madeleine are getting to be good friends. Whenever she calls, we're usually over at the house, and the two of them swap pregnancy tips and dealing-with-adolescent-daughter tips. Madeleine's pregnant as well, it appears, and Megan is going to be the godmother. I expected them to hate each other, you know, the past and future wives of Chris Walsh, but they don't. Adults are weird.

Friday   *12/6/98*

Our school tour to Blessington was yesterday. It was brilliant. Kate, Megan and I were in a group together. Robbie, Trevor and Alan were in the group as well, so whenever we had to split up into smaller groups we all went together.

We did canoeing first, and then kayaking. After lunch we did orienteering and archery. I was hopeless at the kayaking. I couldn't steer it, and I dropped my oar at one stage. I also capsized three times. Not even on purpose, like some people did because it was fun, but accidentally.

Orienteering was fun, the six of us were together. We left our map behind at one point and then spent twenty minutes looking for it. My runner got stuck in the mud – it was like quicksand! – and Robbie and Megan had to pull me out, and Kate rescued my runner. It was a good thing they were my spare pair, because they're wrecked now. I wore them into the lake as well, and since I fell in three times, plus "accidentally" falling out of the canoe (we all did that, it was great! When Alan did it we started rowing off without him!), they're a state!

Thursday   18/6/98

I can't wait until the play is over. We have rehearsals every day now. I'm sick and tired of sitting through it. I don't even have to do anything more, but the teachers insist on Aisling and I attending all of the rehearsals. Aisling is going to be the make-up artist for next week – Mr Fitzsimons went into a panic when he realised no one was assigned to make-up! – and I'm not sure what I have to do. Rehearsals are gradually getting more chaotic every day.

Monday   22/6/98

I'm going crazy. I spent most of today staring across the classroom at Robbie. Why? I don't even know myself. He's nice, I suppose, but everyone knows he fancies Maria, the bitch, so there's no point in me even fantasising. But I wasn't. Was I?

I don't know what I'd say even if Robbie did ask me out. I mean, what if he was messing and I said yes and totally humiliated myself? Then again, what if he wasn't and I said no because I thought he was messing? Even if I said yes and he meant it, how exactly do you "go out" with someone? I'm so confused.

Wednesday 24/6/98

The play went okay, I suppose. Everyone was so nervous before it, though. Kate was bawling her eyes out and Amy was chewing her nails down to nothing. Aisling calmed them down, naturally. Everyone always goes to her for support.

Does it sound like I'm jealous? Well, I just figured it out right now. I am jealous of Aisling. She's so perfect at everything. She's really pretty and confident around boys, and she's really smart, and brilliant at singing and playing instruments, and great at writing music and lyrics, and good at sport and art as well, plus she's great at acting as well, I've seen her practising with Megan, doing Kate's part. Plus Aisling's so sensitive and everyone always goes to her for advice or if they're really upset. Isn't that just great? I'm jealous of one of my best friends, because she's the type of person I've always wanted to be.

Thursday   25/6/98

I ran into Robbie at the shops today, before the play started, and he asked me was I going to the disco tomorrow.

"Yeah," I said. "Everyone is."

"Great. So, you have to be at the play tonight, right?"

"Yeah. It's getting to be really boring, actually."

"I bet. Sitting through it so many times . . . well, see you, Alison."

"See you."

It sounds ridiculous to be so cheerful about such a casual conversation, but it cheered me up so much I practically danced into the school hall tonight, and I didn't even care that Aisling was busy being perfect. Kate was with her.

"Someone's in a good mood," observed Aisling.

"Me? Nah," I replied.

"Yeah, you are," Kate laughed. "Okay, let's see . . . you don't have to sit through the play tonight?"

"I wish! Listen, nothing's up."

"Robbie! Did he ask you out yet?" Kate asked.

"Why would he?" I replied.

"Well . . ." she grinned. "He sort of likes you."

"Really?" I said nonchalantly. "Oh." Inside I was screaming, YES, YES!

"Get that casual look off your face, Alison, I can tell you're thrilled."

"Kate! What are you, a mind reader?"

"Ah, so I'm right!"

"Oh, shut up!"

Robbie likes me! YES!

Friday 26/6/98

We all couldn't wait for this afternoon's performance of the play to be over, because of the disco. Some people ran home to change, but me, Aisling, Kate and Amy just brought a change of clothes with us. And there was make-up backstage, anyway, so Amy was pleased. She always wears tons of make-up to discos, and she wears mascara into school sometimes.

Aisling did us all up, insisting that it was our last disco together so we might as well make it special. I felt awfully self-conscious, but the others didn't have that problem.

The boys in our class, including Robbie, sort of edged over to us during the fast dances. Most of my friends are practically professionals at dancing, but I'm not that great. Still, I copied what they were doing. At least I pick up moves quickly.

Robbie didn't ask me to dance for the slow dances, instead, we chatted. I think it was better that way, somehow.

Sunday 28/6/98

Yesterday was even more chaotic than usual. Kate came in with a sore throat, so she and I had to convince Aisling to do her part. Let me tell you, it was pretty hard doing that, gushing over how great she was. It was true, but I'm a bitch – I hate the fact she's better than me at a lot of things.

She did really well. When she was singing I Hate Being Me I felt tears welling up in my eyes, and it wasn't from the lyrics.

Monday   29/6/98

I know I'm going to miss everyone. Well, except Megan! We're moving in soon, and in September we'll be in the same class. I wish we were all going to the same school, though. We'd have so much fun! Still, we're not, so I guess I just have to accept that. And hope for the best.

Wednesday   1/7/98

Just call me Alison Taylor, life-saver. Emma came over today bitching about Aisling. It was about the disco – Aisling met Brian at the disco and apparently Orla fancies him like mad, but Aisling doesn't. Let me tell you, I was tempted to join in and be a total cow about Aisling, but I stopped myself. It wouldn't have been fair to Aisling, and she still is one of my best friends, even if we haven't been particularly close these last few weeks. I stood up for her, saying that Aisling hadn't known and if she had, she wouldn't have danced with him. Emma kind of cooled off and cancelled her plans to march over to Aisling's house and express her oh-so-kind thoughts on the matter.

"You're so loyal to your best friend," Emma said as she was leaving. Yeah, I guess I am. I've finally realised what I've been telling myself for years but never fully registered – I shouldn't feel jealous of Aisling. She's not perfect, even though she seems to be, and she's my best friend. Okay, so she has a lot of talents, but so do I! I wrote a play in less than a month! How many thirteen-year-olds can say that? I'm not boasting or anything, it's just that I've finally gained some self-confidence.

Think the fact that Robbie came over today and we agreed to go together had anything to do with that?!!

3: Amy's Diary

Fact-File

Name:: Amy Johnson

Age:: 12, 13 on March 19th

Family:: Parents and older sister, Michelle, 15

Looks:: blue eyes with blonde hair cut like Jennifer Aniston's

Hobbies:: being the class clown, drawing, painting

Ambitions:: To be an artist or a comedian

School:: Currently at Hillside Primary, going to Hillside Secondary

Friends:: Megan, Aisling, Alison, Emma, Kate, Helen

Worst Enemies:: Donna Jones and her friends

Favourite T.V. programme:: Friends

Favourite Actor:: Leonardo DiCaprio

Favourite Actress:: Jennifer Aniston

Favourite Films:: Titanic, Romeo And Juliet, any film with Leonardo DiCaprio

Favourite Book:: This Place Has No Atmosphere

Favourite Author:: Paula Danziger

Favourite Singer:: Mariah Carey

Favourite Groups:: Backstreet Boys and Five

Favourite Song:: Everybody Get Up – Five

Favourite Album:: Musicbox – Mariah Carey

Wed.   *Feb. 11*

Mrs Lyons was out today. I was in a class with Emma and Megan. When me and Megan get together we act really crazy. Which is why we got given out to about a billion times today.

Alison and Aisling were in a class together as well. They're both really smart and nice. Alison's the writer and Aisling's the musician. Then there's Emma, she's really sporty and fit and healthy and she acts real cool and confident.

My parents were pleased with the result of my history test yesterday. I got 85%, which is good for me. Of course, Alison and Aisling scored in the nineties. I say "of course" because they always do well on tests. It's so unfair. I bet they don't even have to bother studying.

Megan's having a slumber party soon, for her twelfth birthday. I can't wait for it. Then she and Aisling and Emma are going on the school skiing trip. Alison and I can't go because it's expensive – six hundred pounds. It's a week-long trip, and with half the class gone Alison and I will have a good time anyway. And they'll still be stuck with Mrs Lyons, she's going as well.

Thurs.   *Feb. 12*

I feel sort of guilty over what happened today, but not really. You see, Mrs Lyons, who was back in today, was giving out to Aisling, who started bawling crying. Emma and I were talking about how babyish Aisling can be during yard time, and she and Alison and Megan overheard us. Aisling started crying again – what a baby! – and Megan and Alison got all sappy and hugged her.

I wonder what we're going to do about seeing Titanic. We have the tickets and Megan's dad is driving us on Monday night. I bet we'll have made up by Monday. Trust me. Leonardo DiCaprio is in the film.

Fri. Feb. 13

I was right! We're all friends again and we're all going to see the film on Monday night. I told you!

The Valentine's Disco is tonight. I'm not going. I bet it'll be boring. Okay, fine, you got me. No one asked me and I don't feel like standing around all evening.

Sat. Feb. 14

I ended up going to the disco. It was sort of fun. Me, Megan, Alison and Emma hung around talking. Aisling went off with James from our class – lucky her!

Mon. Feb. 16

Shoot me. I mean it. Now Alison's going on the skiing trip – her mum paid for her. That means while they're off having a great time in Italy I'll be here in Ireland, lonely and miserable. I hate my life.

Tue.   *Feb. 17*

The movie was deadly last night but I was still thinking about the skiing trip. Megan, Aisling and Alison turned on the waterworks for the whole film, which was sort of annoying. It was dead long, too – three and a quarter hours! Still, Leonardo DiCaprio was in it . . .

Wed.   *Feb. 18*

I can't believe it. Don't any of my friends care about my feelings? All they can talk about is the ski trip and how much they're looking forward to it. No-one has asked me, "Hey, Amy, how do you feel about being left behind for a week while your best friends are off skiing? And, by the way, do you mind if all we can talk about is the trip?"

Except Aisling. I know sometimes I think she's a little babyish, but she can be such a good friend sometimes. She told me she really wishes I was going, and knew that I was feeling depressed now that Alison's going as well. Sometimes I think she's the nicest of all my friends.

Sat.   *Feb. 21*

I've just come back from Megan's slumber party. We had a great time, watching films, gossiping, painting each other's nails and stuffing our faces! I had to beg my parents to let me go, though – they don't really approve of slumber parties. They never let me have any, just one friend sleeping over

– usually Megan – and they come up with all these ridiculous rules we have to follow or else.

Fri. Feb. 27

I hate my life and they've only been gone two days. I'm with James, Kate, Helen, Trevor and Conor. We're all hanging out together in yard. It's funny, I've been in the same class as them for eight years and I never knew how nice they all were.

Especially James. Now see why I hate my life? I have a crush on my best friend's boyfriend!

Sat. Feb. 28

James called round today – asked if I wanted to go up to the school yard with him and some of the others to play basketball. I said yes – I don't have much to do now with all my friends in Italy. Anyway, there were some more kids from my class and some from others.

I was on a team with James, Kate, Helen, Conor and Trevor. We made a pretty good team – Kate's on the girls' community team and Conor's on the school team.

We won, 24–19. I scored five of those points!

I wonder how everyone's getting along in Italy. I bet they're all having a great time, skiing brilliantly and drinking espresso and eating biscotti and meeting up with some cool Italian guys.

Or, as James suggested, they could hate the skiing, be bored, and have broken arms or legs.

Nah.

Sun. March 1

I'm bored and depressed and miss my friends and I bet they didn't even buy me a present. Okay, Aisling might, but not the others. They're probably too busy impressing people with their incredible skiing skills and flirting with gorgeous Italians and going shopping in those classy Italian shops.

Later

Just as I was saying how bored and depressed I was, Conor phoned me and asked would I like to go see Titanic in the Square, as everyone else was going. Today. He'd got his dad to book six tickets and he invited me, Helen, Kate, Trevor and James. His dad drove us up and went somewhere while the film was on.

I had to plead with Mum to let me go. She can be so annoying sometimes. She won't let me do anything. I have to beg her to let me go to discos and slumber parties. She didn't like the idea me going to the cinema with boys. I explained we were all just friends, but she still wasn't convinced. Luckily, Dad came home then, and I can always wrap him around my little finger.

"I'm warning you, I'm gonna cry during this," Helen warned us before the film started.

"You can curl up beside me," Trevor offered. He's such a flirt, once he gets over his nervousness at the start. He fancies Helen like crazy, though. He puts on a macho image all the time, but really he's nice and sensitive. Perfect for Helen, actually, although she doesn't seem to like him.

"That says desperate, Trev," Conor laughed. He nudged Kate. "Doesn't it, Kate? I mean, I don't say that I want you on top of me, but you know that's what I mean."

Did I say Trevor was a flirt?

Kate blushed and laughed. "You're the one who's desperate, Con," she said.

Conor grinned. Then he winked at me. "How 'bout you, Amy? Feel like jumping on top of me? You don't have to ask first."

I hit him playfully on the arm. "In your dreams."

"Or in James'," muttered Trevor.

James turned red. "I have a girlfriend, Trev, in case you've forgotten."

"Who just happens to be one of my best friends, you idiot," I reminded Trevor, raising my left eyebrow at him.

We had a good time. I cried this time – so sue me, but when they start playing that music it just sounds so romantic. And when it got to the end bit when he dies, it really got me.

When we came out of the cinema I was still thinking about the film, and still crying.

"Are you okay?" asked Helen. "Crying that much after a film is not natural."

"Sorry," I sniffed.

We went into Burger King. Conor's dad had given him money to treat everyone – he feels guilty that Conor's not going on the trip.

Then we went around the Square a little bit. Helen, Kate and I went into Accessorize and bought cheap earrings. Mine are purple presents hanging from a silver circle, Helen's are red telephones hanging from a red circle, and Kate's are green shamrocks hanging from gold shamrocks.

We had a great time. Definitely.

Mon.   **March 2**

Me, Helen and Kate wore our earrings in today. The teacher gave out, but who cares? We weren't actually told to take them off, so we didn't.

The six of us were hanging around in yard as usual today. Trevor was flirting with Helen and the rest of us were discussing Titanic. At little break, actually, most of us stayed inside for half of it, and as we went out, Kate and Conor came in, probably for a heavy session of meeting each other. I don't know if they're going together, but they act like it sometimes.

Emma's mum was talking to my mum today – they're friends. Emma broke her arm skiing. Poor her.

There's a disco, Friday night in the community centre. Kate got me and Helen tickets, as she's in the youth club.

Tue.   **March 3**

I'm trying to pretend I don't like James that way but it's tough. Still, all I have to do is talk to Helen or Kate, laugh around with Trevor or Conor and pretend he doesn't exist.

If only he wasn't going out with Aisling! If it was anyone else, maybe even Megan or Emma, I might consider flirting with him and asking him out. But he's Aisling's boyfriend. And I'd feel horribly guilty for the rest of my life if I hurt her again. I miss her, I have to admit.

Wed.   March 4

Kate and Helen came over today. We watched a video of Romy and Michelle's High School Reunion, the one with Lisa Kudrow from Friends, and we were laughing hysterically over it.

I like hanging around with them, but sometimes I feel . . . well, a bit loud. I'm always joking around. Kate usually joins in, but sometimes she's really quiet and thoughtful, which surprises me, because I always thought she was really cool and funny. And Helen . . . well, she's a bit quiet. All the time. We're always telling her to be more confident, because she is really nice. Anyway, they're both sound.

Still, I can't wait for Alison and Megan and Emma and Aisling to be back. I wish I could be at the airport to meet them instead of waiting until Friday to see them – hey! Why don't I? I mean, all their parents are going up to meet them there, so I'll just ask around a bit.

Thurs.   March 5

Well, I was able to meet my friends at the airport. Emma's mum drove me up and back.

You should've seen their faces when I waved to them as

they came in to join their parents. By the way, they all have presents for me, but they're going to give them to me tomorrow, at Alison's birthday slumber party – she'll be thirteen.

Life couldn't be better. Except I still like James . . .

Sat.   March 7

I got some terrific presents. Emma gave me a bag of dark chocolate shapes, Megan gave me dangly silver Italian-flag earrings, Aisling got me a charm bracelet with the national emblems of European countries as the charms, and Alison got me a pasta-shaped keyring, a necklace with European flags as beads, and a big bar of dark chocolate. I love it all! I'm glad they actually remembered I exist, too!

We watched Romeo And Juliet, the one with Leonardo DiCaprio . . . mmm.

Anyway, that's it. Alison got some really good presents and we all pretended to be so jealous now she's thirteen. My birthday's only on March 19th – YES!

Mon.   March 16

Confirmation was today. Lots of relatives came.

Alison's writing a play for the school. It'll be put on in late June. I might try out.

And now the stuff I feel guilty about. You see, Kate, Helen, me, James, Trevor and Conor went ice-skating on Saturday, because we all had so much fun together during the ski trip. Anyway, me and James were hopeless at it, so we held onto each other as we slipped around and then we fell over. Together.

The truth is, we were practically glued to each other. And I think he was just about to kiss me before we fell.

I feel SO GUILTY!

Thurs.   March 19

My thirteenth birthday. I went out to a classy restaurant for dinner with my parents and Michelle, my bitchy fifteen-year-old sister. I was originally planning to have a slumber party, but I decided not to. Mainly because I've been begging for ages and they always answered no.

My parents gave me thirty quid, a pair of gold earrings, and a huge box of After Eights. Michelle got me a poster of all the people in Friends.

Michelle and Mum drank two glasses of wine each. Dad's a pioneer, and of course, I took the pledge at my Retreat last month. I said I wouldn't drink until I was eighteen. It's a pretty hard thing to do, though, with all the under-age drinking around now, and not to mention all the drugs! Still, I can see myself drinking alcohol before I'm eighteen. I just can't see myself taking drugs, because I swear, I will never take anything like that.

Aisling and Alison have been working super-hard these last few days. Alison's writing the school play, and Aisling's writing the music and lyrics for it. I can't believe they'll have it ready by the end of March, but at this rate, they will. It looks like it's going to be part musical, part drama, and part comedy. Alison said that I should try out for the role of Helen, that it'd be perfect for me. Megan, of course, plans to try out for the lead. She's taken drama lessons for years and she even did an ad for TV!

Anyway, I'm a teenager! Wish me luck on the turbulent, tumultuous journey ahead! (No, I didn't really mean that!)

Sat.   March 28

Last night Helen, Aisling and Kate slept over at my house. Kate was really upset – she'd been at a party earlier and someone had tried to tear her clothes off – and Aisling was really sensitive and understanding etc.

I thought, Oh, great. Aisling has to take over my friends.

Then I had to remind myself, I am the one who's got a gigantic crush on Aisling's boyfriend!

The play is almost finished. Kate, Megan and I went over to Alison's house to act one of the scenes out. It felt so right, the three of us acting it out together. I hope we all get parts.

Sun.   March 29

James called over today. We walked over the shop together to get sweets and then I invited him in to watch the film they were showing on one of the movie channels, which was Mars Attacks! We laughed hysterically over it, and (I know this is going to sound sappy) it just felt so right, you know? Like we're made for each other. (Which is absolutely ridiculous because we're only thirteen.)

One thing I can't figure out, is, Why doesn't James feel guilty about hanging around with me so much when he has a girlfriend? Especially when the girlfriend's one of my best friends? I think that means that he doesn't see me that way, but just as a friend . . . and I'm conveniently "forgetting" about the way he looks at me sometimes . . .

Later

I called Alison earlier on. I said, "Hey, Al, feel like coming over?"

She said, "Look, Amy, I can't, okay? I really have to get this play done."

"Well, sor-ry for living!"

"Oh, grow up, Amy. There're more important things in life than messing around." Then she hung up.

I was hanging up myself when I just started crying. And I never – well, hardly ever, anyway – cry. Especially just over a phone call.

But it wasn't that, really. It was the way Alison was talking to me, and acting like I was so immature. She thinks she's so great, and smart, and brilliant, and thinks she knows everything. I hate her!

I wish I could be mad at Aisling, instead. Because then I'd have a reason for having a hopeless crush on James. Instead, I just feel horribly guilty. I wish they'd break up or something.

Wed.   *April 1*

Only two more days until the Easter holidays! I can't wait. We've all sorts of stuff planned, but you know how it is – you never end up doing it.

Today was, The Talk. We had a counsellor in to talk to us, Rebecca, who was around thirty and really nice. She talked to us for nearly the whole day about sex and periods and "emotional development". What was nice about Rebecca is that she knew we knew all about it, so she simply confirmed the facts for us, and she talked about sex openly. I just wish the boys hadn't been there with us. They kept on laughing and joking all through it. Insensitive morons.

We were all asking each other (the girls, anyway!) if we'd got our periods yet, and lots of people seemed really embarrassed about not getting theirs yet, but since only me and Kate have got ours, there was no need, really. Naturally everyone bombarded us with questions.

Thurs. April 2

There's a disco tomorrow night in the community centre. James asked me to go with him to it. I said yes. What else could I say? I fancy him like crazy! Plus he asked me, so it's not all my fault.

Of course, I did hear Aisling saying something about babysitting tomorrow night . . .

Sat. April 4

James and I ended up spending all of the disco together, dancing. He asked me to go with him. And – here's the best bit! – I said, "What about Aisling?"

He replied, "Hey, we broke up two weeks ago. I don't think she'll mind if we're going together."

I was all, "Broke UP? When? Where? I mean, Aisling didn't tell me anything about this!"

"Really? So like, all this time, you've thought I was cheating on Aisling?"

"More or less."

We both started laughing like crazy.

"By the way," he whispered, conspiratorially, "This guy I know from the youth club is moving in next-door beside Aisling. I told him to watch out for her."

"No!" I laughed. "She'll be thrilled."

So that's it. After weeks of guilt, confusion, and awkwardness, it's all settled.

I called Aisling and we had a good laugh over it. She also told me about that boy – she met him last night. I didn't say James had told him to watch out for her! I had a feeling she wouldn't have been all that thrilled, somehow.

I tried to call Megan, but her dad said, mysteriously, that she was "out." I wonder what's up with her. Maybe Alison knows.

Fri.   *April 10*

This was such a boring week. I went to the cinema on Monday with Helen, and went shopping on Wednesday, and that was it. I can't wait until the Easter camp next week. Something to do, at least.

Tue. April 14

Easter camp started today. I did drama first, and Megan was in the group. I didn't talk to her or anything, because she looked as if she wanted to be alone.

During lunch she told us she'd been in Paris for the past week. She'd been visiting her mother, who left her something like eight years ago, and who's now an actress, who lives in Paris.

Wed. April 15

Tricia Hanley and her sister who's in fifth class, Ann, were picking on Kate today. She rushed off. I couldn't blame her, they were saying awful things, and also saying stuff about her dad, who died in January.

I hate to say it, but Kate is always on the verge of hysteria these days. I can understand it, though. After her dad dying so suddenly, and then that awful thing last month with that boy, it's definitely understandable. If it wasn't for Conor she'd go insane. I mean it, about Conor. Today, he went in straight after her and was in there for ages with her. Aisling went in, as well. Aisling and Kate are getting to be good friends, I think. Which is sort of good, because Aisling is just the right person to have around if Kate loses it.

Fri.   *April 17*

I skipped the fourth session today, and so did James, and we went into one of the classrooms to talk. And other stuff!

Emma and I are working together for that project for school. We're almost finished now.

Tue.   *April 21*

I am in such deep trouble. You see, we found out yesterday, in school, that Conor and Orla were in a car crash, so everyone was talking about meeting up after school to do stuff about get-well cards and things like that. On the spur of the moment, I invited half the class over to my house that evening, completely forgetting that my parents and Michelle were going to a dinner party in some fancy hotel. Even if I'd told them about inviting fifteen kids over, I doubt they would have approved.

They left, anyway, just before six, which was good, because shortly after that Alison turned up to help us get things ready, and then Aisling came as well. I hadn't really thought about tidying the sitting-room or anything like that, so it was a good thing they came over. We had bowls of crisps and bowls of Easter egg bits – I had some left over and Aisling brought some over as well. Alison went down to the shops to get Cidona and Coke, and also remembered to get plastic cups – that's Alison for you, always practical.

Kate turned up next, just as we were finishing up the tidying and setting out stuff, and she said it looked like a party. I was happy about that, because two people being in a car crash isn't exactly a way to put everyone in a terrific mood.

At least half the class showed up. It was tough finding room for fifteen people in my sitting-room, but somehow we managed it.

We went into the computer room, and we made get-well-soon cards and printed them out in colour ink, which wasted almost a whole ink cartridge altogether.

At about nine o' clock some of the boys left, and Megan and Alan left together shortly after that. Then it was Carol and Robbie, and Helen and Trevor. Emma, Kate, Aisling and Alison stayed to help me tidy up, and there was a lot of tidying up to do. After we were finished, we flopped down on the couch and floor and finished off the Cidona and Coke and crisps and chocolate. They all left at around ten o'clock.

That was all fine, but this morning bitchy Mrs Devlin "popped over" to say hi to my parents and asked, "So, how did Amy's party go last night?"

I explained to them what had happened, very calmly, and I added that they'd all been out of the house by nine, and that they'd assumed my parents were upstairs, and that I'd tidied up everything and everyone had stayed in the sitting-room.

That was the truth, well, more or less, but I get no pocket money for next Saturday and the following Saturday, and from now on I'll have to have a babysitter the next time they're out of the house until late.

At least I didn't get grounded. Things could be worse.

Sat.   *April 25*

I'm just back from the hospital. Helen and me went in to see Conor and Orla. A group went in earlier to see them, as well.

Conor has a broken leg, and he'll probably be in the hospital for another few weeks.

"Trevor's been really upset about this," Helen told him as the two of us sat on those horribly hard hospital bedside chairs.

"I know. He was in here earlier with Alan. Emma came in, as well, oh, and Aisling."

"And Kate," I grinned.

"Shut up, you," he said, laughing.

We went in to Orla as well, who's just down the hall from him, and she told us she'll be back in school next week. And she'll be able to go to the Gaeltacht next week.

Wed.   *April 29*

I was such a nervous wreck today. The auditions were on. Luckily I got sent to Aisling for the singing and Alison for the acting, instead of the two teachers, and they were both really nice to me. And I got the part of Helen!

Tricia Hanley, that bitch, tried out for the same part, and she kept on whispering to me, "You know I'm going to get it, so why don't you just piss off?"

As it turns out, she didn't make it past the acting part, but she still followed us, who got through, over to Aisling.

We told Aisling straight off that Alison had told Tricia she hadn't got through.

"That is such a fucking lie," she snapped.

"Maybe it is, maybe it isn't," Aisling said coolly. "Sing for me."

She looked blank. "Like what?" she sneered.

"In case you're thick or something, for any audition, especially when you know it will require singing, you should always have a song prepared."

"That is the biggest load of shit ever."

"Fine. You think it is? Bye."

When Tricia kept on standing there, like the thicko she is, Aisling fixed her glare on her. "Are you thick or something, Tricia? Bye. As in, get lost. Take a hike. Preferably before I get Mr Fitzsimons over here."

Tricia finally got lost, and Aisling sighed. "Okay, listen up while I sing this."

After my audition, Aisling and Alison got me, Kate and Megan to help them out for the rest of the day.

I didn't tell my family about this, I wanted to keep it a secret in case I didn't get the part. I told them at dinner, and instead of being impressed and congratulating me, Mum started on at me about "Are you sure you can handle the responsibility?" and "I'm not sure I like the idea of you spending so much time up there after school" – as if she thought we were going to be hanging around the back of the school drinking or something! – and "What about your homework?", "What about keeping your room tidy?", "What about all your chores?" I expected her to be happy for me and proud of me, but no. Sometimes I hate my mother. Eventually she said it was okay, but still no congratulations. I hate my life.

Tue.   *May 5*

So, here we are in the middle of nowhere in Donegal, speaking weird Irish and having to follow ridiculous rules. I hate it. Everyone else seems to be having a great time. I'm in a room with Kate, Helen and Emma and they all love it.

We had a céilí earlier on. We had to do stupid Irish dancing, and everyone seemed to love it. What is wrong with them? Normally they wouldn't be seen dead dancing around like that.

"Get into the spirit of things," said James while we were dancing.

"Get a life," I retorted.

Megan is teasing me now because she found out I put on mascara every morning. Well, so what? It's clear, and anyway, it always makes me feel more confident and when I know I look good, I'm in a really good mood . . . And I need all the good moods I can get on this trip.

Thurs.   *May 7*

It's still awful. We've translated pop songs into Irish – by the way, when you're singing My Heart Will Go On in Irish you feel incredibly stupid – and done Irish plays, and what was that other thing we had to do? Oh, yeah, write a review of any film we'd seen and thought was good in

Irish. That was fun, actually. I did mine on Titanic, because we'd done lots of phrases I needed in school, so it was dead easy.

That's about the only good thing, though, besides being with my friends, I mean. We stayed up late talking, and we were ages going on about our boyfriends. Alison and Emma, of course, were looking all cool and very I'm A Modern Woman, I Don't Need A Boyfriend because they're the only two without boyfriends. Emma's a total flirt and all the boys in our class are probably too thick for Alison, as she's a total brainbox. Orla, apparently, is going with Seán Miller, who's nice, I suppose. He's one of the Crowd, you know, along with Conor, Trevor, James, Brian, Robbie, Mark, and Alan.

Anyway, we also talked about our parents, whining on, and Kate kind of got upset then, so we changed the subject.

I feel sort of upset at night, I don't know why, but I have to try and control myself or else I know I'm going to start crying, and then everyone would be at me asking what was wrong, and I honestly wouldn't be able to tell them. I wonder what it is. It feels weird. I'm going to blame it on hormones – my excuse for everything. I'm a teenager, after all, I have every right to be moody, in fact, it's almost what's expected of me. I'll tell that to my parents the next time they tell me to stop being such a grouch.

Mon.   May 11

First rehearsal today. It took ages! We were given our scripts and booklets with the music and songs, and we acted out

some scenes, and sang some of the songs. We messed around
a bit as well, our group, as we were away from the teachers
and the younger kids. It was mostly sixth class, and lots
from our class – me, Kate, Megan, Alison, Aisling, Alan,
Brian, Carol. But I suppose since the two main organisers
are in our class we're more interested than the rest.

Lots of people are doing stuff like costumes and props.
And some people are working on the programme and doing
stuff like writing short pieces about the play for the community newsletter and stuff like that. There's also a few
people playing instruments.

Megan and I did a scene where we have this huge fight,
and we actually had to pretend to hurt each other. At the
end, we were cracking up. Mr Fitzsimons was laughing as
well, so we didn't get into trouble. I can already tell that
this play is going to be so much fun!

Tue.   *May 12*

Emma and I had a major fight today. You see, we're both
on the committee for organising the end-of-school disco
for sixth class, and this morning we got into a stupid argument over tickets or something. Then it got worse as the
day went on, and I was so miserable for the whole day. I
was actually crying during break time because I was so upset.
Everyone's trying to not take sides, but it's going to be hard.
I've a feeling this fight isn't going to be a minor one.

Fri.   *May 15*

Okay, well, me and Emma are friends again. We didn't exactly say sorry to each, it was more like little non-verbal ways of saying sorry, like picking up each others' books when Brian purposely knocked them down, and making sure each others' coats didn't fall into the bin (trust me, it happens a lot. You try keeping the classroom bin under the coat rack and see what happens), and stuff like that.

The play is going okay. Some of the songs are really hard to learn. I was talking to Kate and Megan, and we're all, more or less, a bit worried about the singing parts. It's especially hard for me. At least they're in the choir, and used to singing this much. It's exhausting!

James is getting really annoying about me spending so much time on the play. I told him he should work on props or something. He just grunted. When I think of all the emotional trauma I went through to go out with him . . . He's starting to get on my nerves.

Thurs.   *May 21*

Drama at Hillside continued! First of all, the row between Megan and Alan at rehearsal – they never fight! Then over to Kate's house for a quiet evening with a group from the class, to find out that Trevor's mum is dying of cancer! He was crying for ages. Then James, my ever-faithful boyfriend, on the way home, started on about the play again. I told him to get lost – well, except in not such polite terms (screaming "fuck off!!!" at him wasn't exactly mannerly!)

and we ended up having this huge row. Bad couple vibes, that's what me and Megan say. I phoned her and she came over, and we had a girl-to-girl talk, then we chatted about the utter immaturity of boys.

Mon. May 25

Will someone please tell me what is going on here? Today was dramatic as well. Tom Wilson came in today in his usual mood – "I couldn't be bothered", "Fuck off", etc. Then he had to pick on Trevor first, who's even more upset about his mum. He bashed Trevor's head against the wall and then went off to someone else. Trevor started crying – who wouldn't after something like that? – and we all crowded around him.

"Are you okay?" Conor asked him gently. "Trev? Are y'okay?"

"I'll be fine in a sec," he sniffed.

And he was. Until Tom did it to him again during yard, and Trevor sneaked back into the classroom. Me, Helen, and Emma were in, setting the paint and stuff out for art.

"What happened?" Helen asked him.

"Was it Tom again?" Emma asked. When he nodded, she rushed out to the yard. I heard from Megan afterwards that she beat Tom up. She's amazingly strong, and she just . . . well, beat him up! For the rest of the day everyone was teasing him because he was "beaten up by a girl".

Anyway, Trevor was all upset, per usual, and Helen was really concerned about him, and she did all this stuff like stroking his hair and all that, and it was just so romantic, or at least to me it was.

Which makes me feel even more depressed about James. No, we haven't spoken to each other. And we probably never will.

Later

Aisling called. James asked her out. I suppose that means we're finished, then. Anyway, Ash said no. But it's so obvious – he still likes her. I know it's not Aisling's fault, but I can't help feeling hostile.

Wed.   *May 27*

Mrs Lyons was a bitch to me today. I was wearing nail varnish, which I know is against school rules, but practically everyone breaks it anyway. I had them painted very artistically – alternating purple with turquoise glitter and dark pink with gold glitter, with nail transfers on my thumbs. She went nuts when she saw them. Okay, so maybe they looked a bit too cool for school, but still. Aisling, Kate, and Megan complimented me on them as soon as they saw them.

James is still being a bit quiet. I'm positive he still likes Aisling. It's not fair! I know that sounds horribly immature but it's true! She's gorgeous and talented and smart, with lots of boys wanting to go out with her, and I'm just the ugly, unpopular class idiot.

Megan says I'm being insecure. Well, so what? If James is choosing between me and Aisling it's obvious who he'd pick.

Thurs.   **May 28**

I wish there was some drug available to prevent getting your period. I really do. I've only got it a few times, but it's a pain in the neck. Actually, to be exact, a pain in the stomach, in the back, and occasionally in the upper legs.

Naturally this is making me feel even more insecure. Bloody mood swings.

Later

God, I hate my mother! Michelle and I were fighting, and she comes in and starts yelling at me without even hearing what our fight was about. It was completely Michelle's fault. Mum wouldn't even listen to my side of the story! She's such a bitch! She always does that, takes Michelle's side, and she never listens to me. It's like she doesn't care what I think or what I feel, it only matters what she wants. I hate her, I really do.

Fri.   **May 29**

We all went to the disco tonight. It was very dramatic. I wore my Suss bottoms and borrowed a terrific top from Megan, and I looked deadly. James and I went off for a while, until Kate and Conor had that fight and we had to go over and play diplomat. They finally got back together, anyway. Then James and I were dancing, and I caught him staring at Aisling! I burst into tears and hurried out before anyone could see me, but naturally Aisling The Sensitive had to come out and see if I was okay. I yelled at her a bit, and she got upset, and then we made up. It's not her fault if James likes her. But I'm still annoyed with him.

Mon.   *June 1*

James and I split up, broke it off, decided to be "just friends", whatever you want to call it. The point is, I was getting so fed up with him liking Aisling, so I told him to get lost, and we decided very civilly to break up. I think he was going to go over to Aisling and ask her out ... but the look she gave him, it was practically terrifying how icy she got! Then I went over to her and we exchanged smiles, and walked off, leaving James standing there, looking pathetic.

Later

I was just reading my diary from fourth class, and I just realised, back then, it was so important that I liked a boy. I remember Megan and I talking about it. Now it doesn't seem as important, it's okay if you don't fancy anyone for a while. In fact, I feel about most of them, I just want to be friends with them, nothing more. That just occurred to me. I'm not even depressed about James anymore, because, when I think about it, I only really liked him when I didn't really know him all that well, just the good parts.

Fri.   *June 12*

I've been so busy lately, with the play, plus the disco ... I need a break! I've also helped Kate and her mum out a bit with their house. Mrs Long set me free with what used to be the guest room, and I did a terrific job on it, if I do say so myself, but they both said it looked great, so who am I to argue?!

Our school tour was yesterday, to Blessington. It was good, I suppose, except that we were all split up into different groups. At least I was with Aisling and Emma. Whenever we had to form teams, like for archery, or orienteering, or the canoeing, we stayed together, and then the boys joined us. James was with us, and so were Conor and Brian. We had so much fun during the orienteering, splashing through the muck. We all pushed each other into it, and afterwards our tracksuits were wrecked. At least it was the last activity of the day! I took a photo of the six of us, all covered in muck. I can't wait until it gets developed!

Oh, and during the windsurfing, Emma went on a board with Conor, so Aisling and I could share. The six of us were all crashing into each other and pushing each other off. And during the canoeing, as no one's allowed swim in the lake, we "fell out". We all did it at the same time, and then most of us couldn't get back up onto the boat again. It nearly capsized with all of us leaning on it trying to get in!

Later

Michelle is being such a bitch! Just because she's in the middle of her Junior Cert exams, she thinks she has the right to go around telling us to be quiet, she needs to study. She wouldn't let me watch my Friends video because "the sound of the canned laughter disturbs her studying". I pointed out that if she'd been doing the work she was supposed to all year she wouldn't have to study so much now, right in the middle of it. She snorted and gave me a superior look before walking off.

Sun. *June 14*

We went out for dinner today, to Kingswood Country House. It's on the Naas road, I think. Michelle was complaining, naturally. Apparently it's fine for her friends to drag her away from studying but not for her family. Then she started on about how she hated the food, and before I knew it she and Mum were screaming at each other with everyone else in the restaurant watching in fascination. It was incredibly embarrassing. She's a selfish cow. Actually, both of them are.

Tues. *June 16*

Now we have practices every day after school. I don't really mind. I like playing such a bitchy character. If I'm annoyed, I can blow off steam without really fighting with anyone. Very useful, considering Michelle is still being a cow.

Wed. *June 17*

Plans for the disco are going ahead brilliantly. Even if there's a power cut or there are gate crashers, we'll know how to handle it. I just hope everything goes well – if not, everyone will hate us!

Only a week to go until the play is on. I have to admit I'm nervous.

Fri.   *June 19*

I wish the holidays would hurry up and get here! I feel like I've been waiting forever. We hardly do anything in school anymore, and no one wears in their full school uniform anymore. Mostly we wear navy or black shorts with navy or white t-shirts. We're allowed when the weather gets hot. But some people wear in whatever shorts and t-shirts they feel like. Mrs Lyons has given up giving out to us over it. We only have another week and two days left of school, anyway.

Tues.   *June 23*

We had a dress rehearsal today. Everything went really well. Aisling did the make-up and Emma stayed after school so she could help us change into our different outfits backstage. We didn't forget any of our lines, no one went off-tune, no one forgot how they were supposed to move. The final scene, when we all sing Your Friends Are Always There For You, went perfectly, and we usually mess up when we go into harmony. We're going to be great!

Thurs.   *June 25*

Amazingly, last night and tonight, we did all our scenes perfectly, sang loudly and clearly, and everyone clapped for ages! It went brilliantly, even Michelle the Cow had to admit that.

Fri.   *June 26*

There was a rush after the play finished this afternoon. We only had about an hour between the end of the play and the start of the disco, so some of us just brought a change of clothes with us. We changed backstage, and used some of the make-up we'd been wearing onstage. We all did ourselves up and we looked fantastic.

I had to be there early, anyway, because I was on "door duty" – checking if everyone who came in had a ticket and was in sixth class. Emma was there with me, because she knows everyone in sixth. We had some trouble after a while. A crowd of older boys tried to get in. We had to get Megan's dad to come out and deal with it, because they wouldn't get lost.

James asked me to dance. I know I should've told him to get lost, but with that adorable smile of his, it was impossible to resist. I was worried about what Aisling would think, but I didn't need to – she was too busy getting off with Brian!

Okay, so I shouldn't have spent most of the disco meeting James. (Well, duh!) But I did, okay? He's nice and he's gorgeous and he's fun, and he can be considerate when he wants to be. I'm not saying I'm going to go out with again, but for tonight, he was okay.

Sun.   *June 28*

Our last performance of the play last night! It seems hard to believe. We put so much effort into it and now it's over.

Afterwards, we had a party in the hall, which was great. We definitely deserved it!

It feels weird now, not having to play a character half the time. I find myself turning back into Helen, being mean and bitchy all the time. Mum is definitely bringing that side of me out. She's being so annoying. It's like I can never have a happy home life. I'm either fighting with Michelle or Mum, with Dad groaning and saying he's not going to get involved in this and then turning back to his newspaper. Mum doesn't even try to understand me. I swear, when I'm a mother I'm going to be super-nice to my kids and all their friends will love my house because I'm so nice and I'll always remember what it was like to be their age and I'll always understand what they're going through and know when to give advice and when not to.

Mon.   *June 29*

Second-last day of primary school. I'm going to bring in my camera tomorrow and get tons of pictures. I have everyone's phone number. It's hard to believe I'll hardly ever see all the kids in my class again. Even Emma and Orla, who are going to Hillside Secondary with me, won't be my good friends, probably. They're not going to be in my class – the classes are arranged alphabetically. Kate will, though, and we're doing the same languages as well.

By this time tomorrow I'll be in Spain. The plane leaves at five-thirty in the evening. We're staying for two weeks. When I get back I'll have a fabulous tan and tons of expensive foreign clothes!

Wed.   *July 1*

In Spain. The weather's hot and gorgeous and already I'm tanned. (Well, I will be soon.) This is turning out to be a great holiday. I just wish all my friends were here. I'd love to go here with my friends in a few years time. Except by then we'll probably be like total strangers.

Yesterday was our last day of primary school. We all took loads of photos. I know I'll miss everyone, but I'll get over it, I suppose. It's not like it's the end of the world – we'll still see each other. We just won't be as close, and Megan'll be at a different school. It's kind of scary, isn't it? Going into secondary school, not knowing what to expect . . . God, that sounds so stupid! What I mean is, I don't have a clue what to expect. It'll be fun sometimes, hopefully, and in the meantime, we have two months ahead of us . . . hopefully it won't rain at all!

Fri.   *July 3*

I miss everyone already, and school only ended on Tuesday! It's hard to let go of eight years, I suppose. But you have to at least try, right?

4: Kate's Diary

Fact-File

Name:: Kate Long

Age:: 13

Family:: Dad died recently, older brother, John, 19

Looks:: tall, chin-length dark blonde hair

Hobbies:: Playing basketball on the community team, singing in the choir

Ambitions:: To be a pop star (okay, so what if it's a bit unrealistic?)

School:: In sixth class at Hillside Primary, will soon be at Hillside Secondary

Friends:: Emma, Orla, Aisling, Amy, Helen

Worst Enemies:: Tricia and Ann Hanley (lives on same road as them)

Favourite T.V. programme:: E.R.

Favourite Actor:: George Clooney (so what if he's a bit old?)

Favourite Actress:: Helen Hunt

Favourite Film:: Twister

Favourite Book:: Different Lives

Favourite Author:: Jane Mitchell

Favourite Singer:: Robbie Williams

Favourite Group:: Boyzone

Favourite Song:: Angels by Robbie Williams

Favourite Album:: Said and Done (Boyzone)

Sometimes I feel so miserable I just want to put my head down on my desk and cry my heart out. Actually, I did do that at the start, and everyone was very sympathetic and understanding. But a whole month has gone by since Dad had that awful heart attack and died and now everyone thinks that I'm a baby if I burst out crying.

My friends aren't all that sympathetic. Everyone was, at the start, and sent polite little notes and were very nice around me. But now, Emma and Orla just tell me to get on with my life.

See. Now here I am, bawling my eyes out.

Later

Okay. I've calmed myself down now. I hate this, so much. You'd think I'd feel better after four whole weeks but instead I feel worse. I hate my life.

He died the day after my thirteenth birthday. I can remember that day clearly, every minute of it. Mum and I were out shopping in the Square, with my birthday money, and Dad opted to stay at home. When we got back, we found him on their bed. I remember panicking, screaming, sobbing, as Mum called an ambulance. I still have nightmares about it, seeing him so still on the bed . . . I want so much to talk to someone about this, do something to ease the pain, anything!

Welcome to the Johnston Central Library

Customer name: Antonakis Natasha
Customer ID: 20018000121267

Title: Thirty two C, that's me
ID: 30018002107478
Due: 10/11/07

Title: Dear diary
ID: 30018001904412
Due: 10/11/07

Title: Afterwards
ID: 30018001904172
Due: 10/11/07

Total items: 3
10/20/2007 4:12 PM

Thank you for using the self issue system
Please retain this receipt

Tuesday   *February 10*

Conor Jeffries. Yep, the last person I would have expected to come over to my house after school today and be more sympathetic and understanding and concerned than Emma and Orla have been in the last few weeks.

I've always thought of Conor as a flirt. Which he definitely is. But today he surprised me. He called over to my house about twenty minutes after school had ended. I answered the door. My mum was at work, and my brother was at university. (He's nineteen.)

Anyway, you can imagine my amazement when I opened the door and saw Conor standing there, in his jeans and Adidas sweatshirt, looking uncomfortable but determined to stick with it, I practically collapsed.

"Um . . . Kate . . . I just came over, you know, in case, you . . . um . . . wanted to talk to me about your dad . . . you know . . . oh, forget it, I'll just go . . ."

"No, come on in, Conor."

So, anyway, we were sitting in the living room, and Conor was telling me all about his aunt, who died about a year ago. They were really close; she lived just up the road from them. So he knows what I'm going through. (Doesn't that sound like a really bad line from a really bad movie?)

Anyway, then I was telling him about my dad, and I just burst out crying. He handed me a cushion. "Tissue," he said solemnly. I giggled through my tears. "You're a nutcase."

At the end of the tunnel
Which was gloomy, dark and sad
There was a point of light
Which made it seem not so bad

I never write poems. Which is why that one's so bad. But it sums up everything I want to say.

Wednesday   *February 11*

I was at choir practice today. I sing in the seconds, which is harmony. I'm the only person from my class in the seconds, so in the few minutes before choir started, I was over talking to Aisling Molloy and Megan Walsh, who're in the descants. They're sort of my friends, but we're not really close. I mean, Aisling did send me a very thoughtful note after my dad died, and Megan and I went to the Tuesday French class last term and sat together, but apart from that we're not all that friendly. I've always wanted to get to know them better, though. Megan is this really talented actress and Aisling is perfect at everything – school, music, art, sport.

Anyway, I was talking to them, about the episode of Friends that had been shown on Monday, when suddenly I got this lump in my throat, the way you do when you're going to cry, and I had to stay quiet for a few minutes.

"Are you okay?" Aisling asked me, looking worried.

I swallowed. "Yeah, I'm fine. Listen, I gotta go now."

I don't know what on earth got into me. I'm sure Aisling and Megan think I'm a total weirdo now, I could see them whispering after I went back over to my seat.

Thursday   *February 12*

Mrs Lyons told us who would be in what classes while the skiing trip was on. I really should explain. The skiing trip to Italy is a week long, and about forty of the hundred and twenty-something sixth class are going on it. It starts in two weeks. Orla and Emma are both going. I found out who I'm going to be in a class with – Trevor White, Amy Johnson, Helen Murray, James Robinson, and Conor. Pretty good. Trevor is nice, if a bit annoying occasionally, and James is good fun. As for Amy . . . she's absolutely great fun. She has a great sense of humour. Then there's Helen. I don't really know her that well. She hangs around with another girl in our class, Carol, who's bossy and a bit bitchy. She bosses Helen around no end, and acts as if she's the greatest and Helen is her slave. Helen seems okay, apart from being pretty quiet, and I really should give her some advice – "Get a life and stay away from Carol!"

And Conor. We haven't exactly spoken to each other since Tuesday, and we try not to look at each other. I suppose it's because we both have an "image" at school – that we're cool, and that we never talk about all that stuff. I think a lot about "images", as a matter of fact. Like, for example, Emma seems really cool and controlled and confident, but I've seen her crying her eyes out or totally losing her temper. Orla seems the same, and most of the time she acts like that, but I know how much she hates feeling grown-up.

I probably sound like a psychologist or something. I'm going to watch TV.

125

Friday   *February 13*

I bought the Titanic soundtrack today, in HMV, for £15.99. I haven't seen the film yet, but I hope to, soon. Anyway, I've been listening to it. It's mostly music, except for the song Celine Dion sings. I'm normally not into just music without lyrics, but the album's really cool.

Saturday   *February 14*

I went to the disco in the community centre last night, the Valentine's one. I got all dressed up, in a tight red top, a black mini-skirt and black tights. (Mum almost didn't let me out of the house! I didn't look tarty, though, thank God!) I was a bit self-conscious at first, because the outfit was so tight, but I'm pretty skinny, so after a while I got used to it. Conor came up and said I looked great. He was in jeans, like most of the other boys there. It's always the same, the girls all dressed up and the boys in jeans or rip-offs or tracksuit bottoms.

"So we'll be in the same class during the ski trip," I said, feeling pretty stupid, but it was all that I could think of.

"Yeah. I can't wait. It'll be a doss week. We can finish all the work she gives us on the first day and then mess around for the rest of the week."

"Sounds great," I murmured. I looked out at the kids dancing in the middle of the hall.

"Ah, look, there's James with Aisling. I knew he'd ask her eventually," Conor grinned.

I saw them, Aisling and James, practically super-glued

to each other. I couldn't imagine them together, actually. Aisling is this beautiful, popular, smart musician, and James is a not-so-smart, sport-crazy clown.

"Hey, feel like dancing?" he asked me.

"Can't dance," I muttered. Suddenly I was all self-conscious and shy. Strange, for me. What is happening to me?

"No problemo. I can't either. Just like everyone else out there." A fast song was playing and everyone was messing around. So we joined them.

Then they played a few of the slow ones, and Conor and I sort of looked at each other awkwardly and then edged towards the wall. We didn't actually go back to dancing after that. We just leaned against the wall, and chatted about superficial things and the kids in our class and all that stuff.

I kind of wish we'd gone for the slow dancing.

Sunday   February 15

I'm bored. Incredibly bored. I can't imagine what it'll be like during the skiing trip when Emma and Orla are away.

I just walked over to Emma's, but she was out with her other friends. And it's impossible to do anything in Orla's house. With such a big family, there's always a few of them around to annoy us.

Thursday   February 19

Our Retreat was today.

I'm just back from the Square. I went to see Titanic.

There is one thing I want to know. Why wasn't this film made sooner? It is absolutely positively the greatest film I have ever seen in my entire life. Of course I was crying like a baby though it all, but that's practically required.

Monday   *February 23*

Our Ceremony of Light is tomorrow. I'm a bit worried about what to do – no one has told us or shown us, and we haven't discussed it at all in school. All Mrs Lyons will tell us is that we need our baptismal candles.

John is at the RTC so I can't ask him about it, and I don't think they had this ceremony when Mum was growing up. Everyone else has older brothers or sisters who have told them about it, or else they were in the choir last year and sang at it. This year, the choir aren't singing, so that's one thing I don't need to worry about. Anyway, I wasn't in the choir last year, so I have no idea what to do.

Tuesday   *February 24*

It's ten-thirty and I'm practically asleep. The Ceremony of Light ended at nine o' clock. It turned out to be okay.

Conor's mum and mine were chatting away to each other. It turns out they shared a room at college and worked together for a few years, and when they found themselves sitting beside each other they began their trip back down memory lane.

We arrived in the church about fifteen, twenty minutes early. It was crowded, though. Conor and I were trying to look past our chattering mothers. There was a dangerous moment when they were chatting and Mum told Conor's mum about Dad, and I almost started crying right then. Conor knew exactly what was up and he gave me a sympathetic look. He's so sound.

We'd made paper plates and cut holes in them to slip the candles through, to avoid the hot wax dripping down onto our hands. Most people had the thick candles with the sort of crater at the top so that the wax formed a little puddle in it and didn't drip, but I had one of those skinny candles with the wick on the very top of the candle, so the wax got all over the place. Also, I forgot what Mrs Lyons said about keeping the lit candle upright while you're passing on the flame, so the wax dripped onto my skirt.

It was funny, though. Mr Maguire sang – yes, sang! – and he sounded awful! I had to bite into my lip and dig my nails into my hands to stop myself laughing. I looked at Conor during that song and he was doing the same.

Then there was the – hmm, I'm not sure what to call it. A mime, maybe, or a creative movement thingy. Whatever it was, it involved all of room eleven moving their hands and arms about in a very stupid-looking way. I couldn't help myself laughing through that, and half the kids around me couldn't either. Some of the parents looked very disapproving, but so what?

Wednesday   *February 25*

I walked home from school with a big group from school today. Let me see, there was . . . well, me, of course, and

Orla, Carol, Helen, Trevor, James, and Conor, and a few more from the other sixth classes. Carol kept on yapping on about her outfit she'd bought for Confirmation and about all her relatives that were coming, blah blah blah. We were all looking at each other, thinking, would she ever shut up!

Some of us tried to get a word in, but she just said, "Hold on a sec, I'm talking here. Honestly, you're so rude." That girl definitely needs a personality transplant before we all kill her. I felt sorry for Helen, who was hanging around the edge of the group, knowing exactly how annoying Carol was being, but being too shy to tell her to shut up, which is what I would have done. I'm usually not rude, but Carol is so mean!

We had choir today, for nearly two hours. A few people were missing, because we're practising for the music festival in the Basketball Arena in Tallaght. It's on during the skiing trip, so anyone who was going was told not to bother coming to the practices for it.

Friday   *February 27*

So far, so good. Helen, Amy, James, Trevor, Conor and I are getting along great, and we have our own group of tables at the back of the classroom we're in. Half the time I'm at choir, of course, practising like crazy, but the other half we're all messing around and having fun.

Amy is so funny, she gets me cracking up every two seconds. James is a bit quiet, but fun, and Conor is just . . . Conor. And I have a huge crush on him.

Trevor is a bit of a flirt. Actually, forget "a bit of". He's a flirt-a-holic, plain and simple. But I know he's a bit of a softie at heart. He has a gigantic crush on Helen, by the way, and he's really nice to her. Helen seems like she doesn't like him, though, or maybe it's just that she's shy around him.

Another choir practise today, naturally, and the girl who was supposed to do a solo is sick, so Miss Devlin is getting me to sing it. I can't wait!

Sunday   March 1

This is turning out to be fun, actually. Even though Orla and Emma are away skiing, I'm still having a good time with the group.

Yesterday we went up to the school yard to play basketball, and we had lots of fun. I love basketball – I'm on the community team, and every chance I get I go up to the yard with Emma or Orla and practise shooting.

Today we went to the Square. We went into the cinema to see Titanic. It was brilliant, naturally, and I enjoyed it as much as I did the first time. I sat in between Conor and Trevor, and I was sort of leaning towards Conor. By the way, I told you Trev was a softie and I have been proven right – he was actually crying during the film. Conor, on the other hand, is a real man. (Well, sort of).

We went to Burger King afterwards, and then looked around and shopped a bit. Helen, Amy and I went looking at jewellery, and we bought some cheap earrings. We had a lot of fun messing around with them, and the shop assistant was giving us evil looks as we hadn't bought anything yet.

Monday   *March 2*

Today the three of us – me, Amy, Helen – were joking around and having a lot of fun, but I was faking it. I had a nightmare last night, about everyone I know dying, which reminded me of Dad.

Conor noticed something was up. "Are you okay?" he asked me in yard. The two of us were outside, the other four were staying inside, with the warm radiators, even though they're not allowed.

"I'm okay. Sort of," I lied, but I was getting a big lump in my throat. And I was trying hard to stop shaking.

Conor looked at me sceptically, then he said, "Come on, it's freezing out here. Let's go in." But he gave me a look that told me that he knew that I was about to cry and that I would be incredibly embarrassed if I cried in front of the whole yard.

The two girls, I call them the Gruesome Twosome, who are in charge of locking and opening the side doors of the school, glared at us when we walked through.

"Do you have permission to go in?" one of them asked. Davinia, I think. Can you imagine having a name like that?

Anyway, I was on the verge of tears, so Conor spoke up.

"Well, duh," he snapped. "We wouldn't be going in otherwise, would we?"

That put Miss Do-You-Have-Permission in her place. I managed to smile weakly at Conor as we walked up the corridor to our classroom. Well, not our classroom, but the classroom we're in for the week. Helen, Amy, James and Trevor were just walking out the door and into the yard.

We passed them by and I kept my head down. I didn't want to let them know I was upset.

Once we were in the classroom, I rushed into the girls' bathroom and locked the door.

I'd been in there for a few minutes, crying, when Conor knocked on the door. "Kate? Are you okay?" he asked.

I didn't answer him, but he kept on asking. I was crying too hard to answer.

"C'mon, Kate, come out of there! Yard's nearly over. You might as well come out now before the class comes back in."

He had a point there, so I came out. After all, I didn't want to come out of the toilet with everyone watching and tears pouring down my face.

I walked out of the bathroom, tears blurring my vision, and crashed into the bin and stumbled.

"Hey, take it easy," Conor said, grabbing me around the waist and stopping me from falling. I didn't even notice until he pulled me up and we gazed into each others' eyes, and it was so romantic . . .

And then we both started laughing.

"This is ridiculous," I giggled, drying my eyes on my jumper sleeve.

"I know," agreed Conor. He let go of my waist.

The buzzer sounded for the end of yard, and I knew that any minute everyone else would come rushing into the classroom.

Conor reached out and stroked my hair.

"We'd better sit down," I said softly.

"Mm-hmm," he agreed, and we went to the back of the

classroom and sat down. A few moments later everyone else rushed in. Helen, Amy, James and Trevor sat down at our table.

"Why were you crying?" Amy asked.

My eyes probably looked all red and swollen. Damn.

"Oh, I fell out in yard, and my back is killing me," I lied.

I have SUCH a big crush on Conor. He's just so great. When I was younger, I used to imagine my dream guy, and he's what I imagined and more. But he probably just thinks of me as a friend.

Tuesday   March 3

There's a disco in the community centre this Friday. As I'm in the youth club, I have tickets, and I can get them for anyone I want. I got tickets for Amy and Helen, and I offered to get some for Carol and Aisling and Alison and Megan.

Conor asked if I was going. I said I was.

"Good," he grinned. "See you there. Wear something see-through."

"You are such a flirt!"

"Guilty as charged. But you're just so gorgeous – "

"Yeah, right."

"And sexy," he added, giving me that incredible look.

"Who're you talking about here? Not me, that's for sure."

"You're so modest," he sighed. "We'll have to do something about that."

"We will not have to do something about that, I like myself the way I am."

"Then why d'you keep on putting yourself down?"

"I do not!"

"See you, gorgeous," he grinned, walking off.

God, I love him so much. He wouldn't flirt with me like that if he didn't like me . . . right?

Wednesday   March 4

The six of us were walking home today, as usual, and I was going to the shop, so instead of turning off at my corner I went straight on with Amy and Conor. Amy turned into her house, and Conor and I walked across the road to the shop. He lives in the estate beside the shop, about half a mile away from the school.

The traffic on the road was chaotic, it always is, as it's a main road, and lots of people were coming and going from the school, picking their kids up. Conor and I were left standing there, waiting.

"Want to go to the cinema tomorrow?" he asked me.

"To see what? There's nothing decent in the cinema."

"How about Titanic?"

"I've seen it twice!"

"I know you girls," he grinned. "You won't be happy unless you've seen it three times. Or more."

"That's not true. I could cope without seeing Leonardo DiCaprio for a little while. Until, say, The Man In The Iron Mask comes out."

"Come on, will you go or not?"

"Okay, I will. Call me later, okay? Oh, I'd better give you my number."

"No problemo. I know it." He recited my phone number. "How'd you know that?"

He grinned. "None of your business. Anyway, I bet you know mine."

He had a point there. I do know his phone number. And his address. Off by heart.

He phoned me tonight. We're not going to tell anyone we're going to see the film together – they'd just make a big deal out of it and tease us. We're just going as friends . . . got it? Even though it must be the most romantic film ever, we're just going as friends.

Conor and I were saying that on the phone. Just as friends. Just as friends. I'm kind of relieved in one way, because he is a great friend, but I'm crazy about him!

Friday   *March 6*

Yesterday turned out to be pretty surprising. But in a very good way! Conor and I arrived up at the Square at about eight-fifteen, after getting the bus up, and we bought some sweets and popcorn before going into the cinema.

We were sitting in our seats behind two people who kept on laughing and talking to each other. Conor and I were too, as the ads were showing and the film hadn't started.

Then one of them turned around, and the three of us looked like we were going to have heart attacks. It was Trevor.

"So, who's the girl?" Conor asked, nodding at the head with curly black hair on it.

136

he turned around. "Helen!" Conor and I exclaimed in unison.

For a few minutes we all looked at each other. Finally, I spoke up.

"I didn't know you two were going together," I remarked.

"We're not," Trevor and Helen chorused. "Just friends."

"Unlike you two," Trevor added.

"We're just friends," Conor and I said in unison.

"So, why didn't anyone tell anyone about going to the cinema tonight?" Helen asked.

"You'd slag us," Conor said immediately.

"Same here," added Trevor.

The film started then, so we had to quiet down. I watched in silence for most of it.

About two-and a half-hours through it, Conor slipped his arm around me.

"What happened to 'just friends'?" I whispered, because I couldn't think of anything to say.

"Forget it," he whispered back. "I like this much better."

"Me too." Oh yeah, oh, yeah! I'm crazy about him.

By the end of the film we'd had our first kiss. (And second. And third. And fourth . . .)

Saturday   March 7

Oh, I just don't know what's getting into me. I feel like I'm going crazy. Half the time I feel like bursting into tears, the other half I feel like going nuts and screaming at everyone.

And then there are the nightmares. Sometimes I can

avoid them. Most nights I can't. I'm almost afraid to go to sleep at nights now. Sometimes I dream that there's a huge fire burning everyone, other times it's an earthquake or volcano eruption, other times everyone gets some terminal illness. I'm scared. I wish I could confide in someone, but I don't want to tell Mum, and my friends wouldn't understand, and neither would Conor.

Monday   March 9

I woke up crying last night. This is the only way I can explain it:

> Flames are everywhere
> Burning, burning hot
> Slowly enveloping everyone
> Screams, screams,
> As they are burnt
> And ashes are all that is left
> While I wait
> For the flames to take me.

Tuesday   March 10

I need something to concentrate on, something to put my energy into. Fast. We had an assembly today, and the teachers want to put on a play by the end of the school year. Alison Taylor is rumoured to be writing it, and she probably will – she's the only one in the school who could manage it.

I might try out, is what I'm thinking. It sounds like something you'd read in Cosmopolitan or one of those magazines, but really, it makes sense for me to do something like this, something I wouldn't normally do, just to take my mind off – well, everything. Dad dying, the nightmares, the gloomy atmosphere in my house.

Friday   March 13

Alison Taylor is writing the school play, she was officially chosen today. She was telling us about it, and Amy said, "You should try out for the part of Liz, you really should."

I might do that. It's a big part, a "best friend of the lead" part, but I could handle it. Megan Walsh is probably going to play the lead role. She's a deadly actress, she was even in an ad for TV.

Saturday   March 14

I'm in love. I really really am. Conor is just so amazing. He really is.

The "non-skiers" gang went ice-skating today, and we were all paired off. Trevor and Helen – even though they insist they're "just friends", Amy and James – who really are just friends, because James is going out with Aisling Molloy – and me and Conor. (And me and Conor are way more than "just friends"!)

James and Amy were hopeless at the ice-skating. They kept on falling over. Then there was Helen, who was clinging onto Trevor as he skated around. So sexist.

I was the only one out of the girls who was good at it. Conor and I skated around together, laughing, talking, kissing . . .

By the way, Helen and Trevor are perfect for each other. Helen is getting more confident now and Trevor has stopped flirting with everything in sight.

Monday   March 16

I made my Confirmation today. My cousin Lauren was my sponsor. She's sixteen, and dead nice. She also knew what to do, after all she did make her Confirmation in our church only four years ago and knew what the sponsors had to do.

There was a group of us in a separate aisle, off to the side, near the choir, because we had to sing with the choir. Aisling sang two solos – yes, two! – and she sang them brilliantly. I sang with Julianne Maguire during the Communion.

I got tons of cash! Lots of relatives came, because they had the Monday off for the St. Patrick's Day weekend, and altogether I got £110.

Wednesday   March 18

Okay, I know I've said before, about a million times, how crap I am at poetry. Writing it, I mean. But I've already written two poems in here already, so what the heck? Might as well go the full nine yards, so to speak. Anyway, I just adore Conor so much I have to do something.

Young Love
I bite my lip, nervously smile
Across the room
Does he see me? Does he care?
Then all my worries vanish
As he turns to me and grins
And I feel like
The most special person in the world.
He strides across the room
And seats himself beside me
I gaze into his eyes
And see a mixture of emotions
He smiles at me
And reaches over to tuck a wisp of hair
Behind my ear
And his touch is gentle
It makes me feel completely and utterly whole.

I must be going nuts. I really think I am.

Saturday   *March 28*

The Attack
I smile and look around the room
Searching for a familiar face
But I see none
I want to leave, I hate this place
Why did I come here, anyway?
Suddenly, a leering grin
An arm around my shoulder

A strong smell of vodka close to me
I feel scared, I want to run
But I am frozen to the spot
He grins at me and drags me to
"A special place where we can be alone"
I don't want to be alone with him
I know what he wants to do
But I won't allow it! I won't!
He reaches out to me
I flinch and try to move away
But he won't let me.
I panic, I scream, but no-one hears
Except him, and he doesn't care
He starts to pull at my top, wanting for it to come off!
It tears, I yell at him
For a moment he releases his grasp
I seize the opportunity and run
Run as far and as fast as I can
Away from him.

That poem says it all, but first I should explain. Last night, I was over at Orla's, planning to stay the night, when Emma called over. We were down at the shops when John McCutcheon invited us to a party down in the end house. We agreed, because it was only eight p.m. so we thought it would be okay.

It was pretty rough, actually. Awful music – well, I don't know if you could call it music – blaring out and tons of vodka and beer and whiskey being passed around. Emma and Orla, the idiots, got drunk within two seconds. They were so stupid. What next, drinking vodka through a straw?

Anyway, I was about to leave, when Creepo approaches, drags me off upstairs and tries to kiss me and rips my poloneck in an effort to feel my breasts. I was so scared! He was touching me everywhere, I hated it but I couldn't stop him. You know the way, in books, they always talk about being "paralysed with fear"? Well, I was. I couldn't speak, I was so terrified – I actually thought he was going to end up raping me, which might have very well happened the way he was going.

I finally found my voice and screamed at him. He was distracted for a second, and then I ran out of the house, and almost crashed into Aisling, Amy, and Helen, who were walking on the other side of the road. I told them what had happened. Emma and Orla chose that time to stumble out drunkenly. We helped them get home.

I was on the verge of tears for most of the evening. I slept over at Amy's house instead. As soon as I reached her house, I dashed up to her bedroom and made myself look busy by arranging my sleeping bag.

Amy and Helen went off yapping about something secret, how fascinating, and being really insensitive, left me bawling my eyes out in a room with Aisling, who I barely know. Okay, so I know her, and I would call her a friend, but not a close friend. Close-ish, maybe.

Anyway, there I was, stupidly straightening out my sleeping bag.

"Kate – you can stop that," Aisling said in a friendly tone.

"Okay," I said quietly.

"Isn't that so sensitive of them?" Aisling said sarcastically. She pointed to the closed bathroom door. "They did that on purpose. Why, I don't know."

"Because I'm here bawling crying and they don't want to deal with that."

"Typical. So typical. Dump everything on Aisling." She grinned at me. "Kill me, please!"

"No can do. I'd wreck this gorgeous top." I looked down at my top. "Although it looks already wrecked. That bastard."

"Naughty, naughty, Kate. Here, come here, I want to do your hair."

I knelt on the floor as Aisling brushed out my hair. I surreptitiously dried the tears off my face.

By the time Amy and Helen came back, Aisling and I were yapping away like old friends. I managed to stay under control for most of the night, but when we were drifting off to sleep the memory came back to me, haunting me, terrifying me, and I cried for ages, hoping I could sob the pain away.

Monday   March 30

Only Aisling, Helen and Amy know about what happened at that party, and none of them really know how much it affected me. I don't think I could tell Conor about it, I'd feel too strange. It would sound like I was making a big deal out of nothing.

Have to go now, get dressed for school.

Later

I told him. After school we were sitting on the wall outside his house, just talking, when Conor slipped his arm around me, and that simple thing brought back memories of what that guy did to me, and I started crying. He wanted to know what was wrong, and I told him he'd think it was stupid, but eventually I told him. He just put his arms around me and let me bawl my eyes out, and I loved him so much at that moment, and I just hated that guy from the party so much, but I was so determined not to let that thing affect my life any more than it already has, and I clung even closer to Conor. I love him.

Wednesday   *April 1*

Today was a doss day. We had someone come in talking to the whole class about "growing up" and stuff.

   She made lists on the board – "The Changes That Occur During Puberty", and when she came to the "Girls" column all us girls were looking down at our tables, blushing. She kept on waiting for us to say "breasts" and "periods" but we were so embarrassed, we didn't. Eventually Emma raised her hand and said it. The boys kept on teasing us about how embarrassed we were!

   Rebecca, the counsellor, was there talking about periods for a good half-hour. I paid attention, because I got my first period around February, and I should get my next one soon. Afterwards, in yard, we – all the girls – were asking each other had we got it yet. Amy and I both said we had, and I was kind of surprised Aisling didn't say she had, because she has . . . well, let's just say a developed figure.

Friday   April 3

I felt sick today. I didn't think I'd make it through the day, but we finished at twelve because of the Easter holidays. I must have looked pale or something, because I was asked about ten times was I okay, by Aisling, Amy, Emma, Orla, Conor, Helen, and the rest.

I feel okay now. I'm going to blame it on hormones. Mum says it's "growing pains". Give me a break, through! She blames "growing pains" for everything – mood swings, clumsiness, headaches, fainting, travel sickness . . . the list goes on and on.

Monday   April 6

I'm so bored I tidied my room. Yes, tidied it. I can actually see my carpet now. Oh, and I cleaned off my desk. It's supposed to be white, apparently.

I did all my posters as well. I haven't changed them in ages. I ripped off lots of them, and rearranged the ones I have left. I have a big, life-size poster of Leonardo DiCaprio, who I'm starting to like, on the back of my door, and I have posters of Helen Hunt – Best Actress this year, George Clooney, Robbie Williams, Boyzone, Five, and the cast of E.R. on my walls.

My notice-board is practically bare except for a sheet

with the phone numbers of almost the whole class, and a brochure about the Gaeltacht in Donegal. A crowd of us are going up there for a week in May. I can't wait.

Wednesday   April 15

I really need to get my life under control. I did another lock-myself-in-the-toilet-in-school thing today. The Easter recreational programme started yesterday, which is why I was there.

Ann and Tricia Hanley, Bitch and Bitchier, were saying stupid things, and for my benefit faked a heart attack. Horrible, considering Dad. I went inside and locked myself into the bathroom.

Conor came in and tried to get me to come out, and then Aisling came in and tried as well, so I finally came out. And all I wanted to do was break down and cry and have someone hold me in their arms.

That didn't happen. On top of that, I got my period. Naturally, I didn't have any stuff with me. I had to use Aisling's pads.

Monday   April 20

I'm a wreck. Carol The Stuck-Up-Bitch informed us today that on Saturday Conor's dad was driving him and Orla into town and another car swerved out of control and crashed into their car.

I put on the brave act at school, and when we were all walking home together, and I'm still putting it on, I suppose, trying not to get upset even though my best friend and boyfriend have been in a car crash.

Amy's having a get-together at her house tonight, kind of as a cheer-up thing, I think, and I'm invited, along with half the class.

Later

I'm back from Amy's house. I got there at ten to seven, and Alison and Aisling were already there, just setting things out. Aisling asked me if I was okay, and I nodded, because I suppose I like to seem really brave and cool in front of my friends, even though Aisling has seen me bawling my eyes out.

Alison and I were talking during the week, actually, about Aisling, as she's so "practically perfect in every way" and doesn't even realise it.

Anyway, it felt more like a party, because there was Cidona and Coke and chocolate and crisps set out on the tables in the centre of the room, and for the first half-hour, we talked about stuff that had nothing to do with Conor and Orla. Well, except me and a few others. I went over to Trevor, who was sitting on the floor, in the corner, with Helen.

"Hi," I said softly.

Helen looked up. "Hi, Kate," she said, surreptitiously looking over at Trevor and sending me a signal – Don't try talking to him, he's pretty depressed.

Aisling came over to us for a little while. "So, how are you guys?" she asked quietly.

"Okay," I said. "Considering."

She looked over at Trevor. He was looking down at the ground.

Helen gave her that look. "He's pretty upset," she mouthed.

Aisling nodded and went off.

"He'd better be okay," Trevor said.

"He will be, Trev, he will be," Helen said softly, stroking his arm.

I left them alone to do the lovey-dovey bit and went over to Amy and James. "Nice party," I said.

"Yeah," Amy replied. "So, Kate, you okay?"

"It must be tough," added James, "since Orla's your best friend and you're going with Conor."

"Yeah," I said softly. "Does anyone know anything else about them?"

Amy shook her head. "No. Carol's the only one who knows anything about it, and she's already told us all that."

I talked to Emma as well, but she doesn't seem to care.

I made a card for Orla, with Get Well Soon Or Else on the front, on Amy's computer, and also one for Conor: To The World's Best Boyfriend: Hurry Up And Get Better! I added some of those pictures you can add to it, as well, so it looks great, and it's in colour.

We all have a loose arrangement to go in to see them over the weekend. I don't think a lot of people are actually going to go in, that they're just saying they will. I know I'll go in, though, I've already checked that Mum can take me and what the visiting hours are.

God, what if they're not okay? I don't know how I'd cope. I'm kind of upset now, because Orla and I are supposed to be best friends and we haven't done anything together in ages. We used to be so close, but lately I've been spending so much time with Conor and everyone else . . . oh, God, I hope everything goes okay.

Saturday   April 25

I hate hospitals. Absolutely hate them. But I went today, to see Conor and Orla. Mum ended up driving a pile of us over – me, Aisling, Emma, Trevor, and Alan. We had a whole pile of cards and presents from everyone with us.

I was a total wreck when I went in to see Conor. On the way down the corridor, I suddenly burst into tears, and I was so scared of going in to see how he was. Aisling was with me, and she hugged me and told me, gently, to calm down.

Trevor and Alan came back after a while, after going in to see him.

"How is he?" I asked fearfully, drying my eyes.

"Hey, calm down, Kate," Alan said softly. "He's okay, I mean, he has a broken leg, but that's about it."

I practically collapsed with relief.

"I'd better go and see Orla," Aisling said.

"No! Come down with me to see him, okay?"

"Okay, but if you two start getting – shall we say, intimate, I'm leaving."

"Got it."

Conor was in a room with a few other kids our age. His leg was – what do you call it? Where the leg is pulled up and left sort of hanging there? In traction, I think.

Anyway, he had half the pile of cards and presents on his bedside locker, and I dumped the other half with them.

"Hi," I said and burst into tears all over again.

"Um, hi," he said, a little bit awkwardly. "Hi, Aisling."

"Hi, Conor, how are you?" Aisling took over while I got control of myself. "We've been wondering about you all week. So, how long are you going to be in hospital?"

"A week, maybe two, I don't really know," he replied. "So what've I missed in school?"

"Don't ask. Mrs Lyons insists we pray for you and Orla every morning," I told him.

He groaned. "Do you know if Orla's okay, by the way?"

"We haven't been in to see her yet," I said.

"I'm going in to see her now," Aisling said. "I'll come back and fill you in, okay?"

She took off, and I leaned over towards Conor.

"I'm in excruciating pain," he informed me, sighing. "Especially the leg."

I sat down on the chair beside the bed, one of those really hard wooden chairs.

"I've missed you," I said softly. "I've been worried about you."

"Are you coping?"

"Barely. Trevor's pretty upset about it, too."

"Yeah, I know."

I talked to him for a little while longer, and told him I'd be back in sometime during the week. Maybe on Thursday, we have a half-day because of staff meetings. And the week after – oh, no, wait, I'll be in the Gaeltacht for the whole week.

I went into Orla for a short while, then, and she's fine. She injured her head, I think, but she's okay now, and she's leaving the hospital tomorrow.

Wednesday   29 April

I was so spaced out on Monday I completely forgot the auditions for the play were taking place after lunch. I wouldn't have remembered except for Alison and Aisling reminding me.

Lots of fourth, fifth and sixth class kids were there, trying out for the big parts, and the little kids were trying out for stuff like little brothers and sisters.

Miss Devlin, the choir teacher, and Mr Fitzsimons, the Speech and Drama teacher, were there, plus Aisling and Alison. We had to be able to act and sing. The singing part is where tons of people failed miserably.

I did okay with the singing. I was trying out for the part of Liz, so Aisling took a group of us who were trying out for that part and taught us one of the songs we'd have to sing.

Aisling, of course, is a brilliant singer, and she actually wrote all the music and lyrics for the play, and the song sounded great when she sang it. When she got the ten of us to sing it, it sounded . . . well, bad.

"Okay, guys, listen up," she said. "There are about four songs that you'll have to sing if you play Liz, got it? Miss Devlin has told me to cut out anyone who can't sing. If you can sing, then you can go on to the acting part of the audition. So, shape up, okay? And sing louder."

She sounded exactly like Miss Devlin, or at least Miss Devlin when she's in a reasonably good mood.

We were with Aisling for about half an hour, and at the end she looked really exasperated.

"I can only hear three of you actually singing the words. The rest of you are just mumbling along. Well, you're going to regret it, because exactly three of you are going to even have a chance of getting the part. Christine Quinn, Lauren Norton, and Kate Long. You three can go out into the hall now and tell Mr Fitzsimons you're the only ones who are even being remotely considered for the part of Liz."

We went out to the assembly hall then, and went up to Mr Fitzsimons.

"Is Aisling finished with you, then?" he asked.

"Yeah," the three of us chorused.

"Go over to Alison. I think she's finished with the ones trying out for the part of Helen."

We went over to Alison, who was in a corner of the assembly hall, with Amy and a few others.

"Oh, you're here," Alison said. "Okay, Amy, Sara, Denise and Vicki, go into Room 15. Aisling's going to test you out on your singing."

"How's Aisling?" Alison asked me.

"Exhausted."

"Me too. I've been testing out absolutely hopeless kids with no chance ever since lunch. At least you've already been through Aisling."

We had to act out a few scenes. Then Alison said, "Okay, you all did pretty well. There'll be an announcement over the intercom before the end of the day telling you who got the part. You can go back to your classrooms now."

I waited for a minute. "Did I do okay?" I asked her.

She smiled. "I can't tell you whether you got the part or not. But between you and me, Aisling and I both think you're the best person for the part."

"YES! Thanks, Alison."

"No problem. Oh, by the way, if you want you can hang out here with me until school's over. I'll say you're helping me out."

"It's only half-twelve," I pointed out. "School doesn't finish for another two hours."

"Yeah, but we have our second break in between. Hey, I've got an idea."

She went down to ask Mr Fitzsimons if she could get some people to help her out, and Aisling did the same. They picked me, Amy, and Megan, as we'd all just finished our auditions. Then Alison went down to Mrs Lyons to tell her that Mr Fitzsimons had appointed Amy, Megan, and I to assist her and Aisling.

We had a lot of fun, actually. And I got the part of Liz!

Sunday   3 May

I have all my stuff packed for the Gaeltacht, and I've made sure I have everything I'll ever need, and also some books and stuff to read, in case I get bored. Although the chances of that happening, especially with my friends around, are extremely remote.

Monday   4 May

Well, here we are in Donegal. The area we're in is very
. . . rural. There are lots more houses like this, and the Irish
school, of course, and then there are a few tiny shops and
that's it.

Apart from that, it seems to be okay. We got pizza today
for our dinner, instead of the gross stew or something I was
expecting.

The rooms are big enough, and we decided who would
sleep where by whoever wanted the top and bottom bunks.
Amy and Emma have the top bunks in our room, and
Helen and I are under them. Emma has developed a way
to manoeuvre most of her body down towards me so that
we can talk while still having her legs in her bunk so that
she can pull herself up anytime she wants.

There's only one other room in the house, for students,
I mean, and that's the one that Alison and Aisling and
Megan and Orla are sharing.

Tuesday   5 May

I just miss Conor so much, I mean it. At the céilí everyone
was singing and laughing and dancing and messing around,
and I just felt so miserable. I wish I was at home. I miss
watching Friends and E.R. with Mum. I miss being in my
own room. I love being with my friends and everything,
but it's still not home.

Later

I'm trying to keep busy with all the activities there are going on, because if I let myself think about how homesick I am I'll just start bawling and I'll never stop. I need to talk to someone about it, someone who won't laugh if I start crying in the middle of it, which leaves out Emma and Orla. And Amy and Helen. I could talk to Aisling, I suppose, but she's having such a great time here, I don't want to spoil it for her, especially since Emma told me what a rotten time Aisling had on the skiing trip. And it would spoil it for her, because being as sensitive as she is, she'd be thinking of ways to cheer me up and making sure I felt okay, and that would wreck this week. I guess I'll just suffer in silence.

Thursday   *7 May*

I sneaked into the other room last night and Aisling and Alison were there, talking. "Hi," I said, a bit awkwardly.

"Kate, hi, what're you doing in here?" Aisling asked me.

"Oh, I don't know, just came in to talk, I suppose," I said.

"Missing Conor?" Alison asked.

I got that big silly smile on my face that I get whenever I talk about Conor. "Yeah."

"You're dead lucky to have a boyfriend like that," Alison said.

"And I know it!" I said.

Megan joined in a bit later, and then Helen joined in,

and pretty soon there was a huge chat-a-thon going on in the middle of the night.

I have to hurry down to breakfast now. Or else.

Friday   8 May

I phoned Mum today. She says she can't wait to be finished work – she's a teacher at Hillside Secondary – and she also has this great idea for our house. It's pretty big, and now that there's only me and Mum living in it, with John living with his girlfriend in Tallaght, we have tons of space. She's thinking about turning it into a B&B. She has enough money saved up to build an extension on and get it organised. She says she could have it ready by the start of July if she starts soon. She's already sorted out the planning permission, apparently she's been thinking about this for a while.

The disco's tonight. Aisling and I are going to hang around together and wish our boyfriends were here.

Sunday   10 May

Mum has decided – she's going to go for it. She's already called up someone to build the extension. She says it would be better if we moved all our stuff from our bedrooms downstairs. We've already started. I'm going to move my stuff into the sitting-room, and she's moving her stuff into the back room. It's fun, really. Especially since now I have a couch and a TV in my bedroom!

We have glass doors that separate our dining room and

front room, so no problem there, we can just leave them open the whole time. Mum and I are already starting to sort out the upstairs rooms. We have five bedrooms and a bathroom upstairs, well, actually, two bathrooms if you count the small en suite one, and we've already started doing things like moving the phone that used to be in the master bedroom into the hall, and we've checked out the prices of beds, because we only have two or three. Mum took the double bed downstairs, for herself, and naturally I have mine, and then we just have a few left.

Mum is also saying how she expects me to help out once we get started, with cooking and cleaning and organising. I'm not so keen on that, and when I reminded her I'm totally crap at cooking, she said, "well, you can learn."

I phoned some of my friends, and they think it's cool. A few even volunteered to help out – Amy can actually cook! – and I found out it's not the only piece of news on the grapevine. Alison's mum – who's engaged to Megan's dad – is pregnant. Lucky them, getting a little brother or sister soon. I used to hope I'd have a younger brother or sister. Now I suppose I never will.

Thursday   *14 May*

Mum doesn't waste time! The builders came today, and got started straight away. It's going to turn out great, I know it. Mum looks so happy now, she loves having something to work on.

The sitting-room is now officially my bedroom. It's really cosy. I have the TV, my CD/cassette player and my bookshelf at one end, with the couch and my desk in the middle, and then my bed, wardrobe, and locker at the other end, so that it's like three areas in the one room, almost like an apartment. Especially since the bathroom is between my room and Mum's, so all I have to do is go through the door and I'm there.

Aisling thinks it's great. She came over after rehearsal because I was having some problems with one of the songs. Okay, so I was practically crying because I couldn't get it. So what?

Friday   15 May

Straight after school I took the bus to the hospital. I went to see Conor. He'll be out soon, but I hadn't seen him in ages, with the Gaeltacht and then the play.

"So you actually remembered," he said quietly when I came in.

"What's that supposed to mean?" I asked. "I've been busy, you know."

"Look, I knew this was going to happen sooner or later," he said softly. "You don't have to make excuses. Now that you're all cool and sophisticated, you don't need me around any more." He started to sound angry.

"That's not true!" I snapped. "I think you're just making excuses so that you can break it off with me!"

Then I stormed off, in a huff. I wish I hadn't, now. He'll never want to speak to me again. Oh God, why did this have to happen

Later

Conor rang me after dinner! He said sorry, I said sorry . . .

"It's just that . . . I really like you, Kate," he said. "I suppose I was just scared that you didn't like me anymore."

"No way," I told him. "What I can't figure out is why you put up with me!"

It went on like that for ages. The point is, we're not fighting any more, and I like him even more than I ever have. If that's possible.

Monday   *18 May*

Conor's out of hospital! He's on crutches, and he will be for a few more weeks. He came back into school and we were all thrilled to see him, including me! I wasn't sure when exactly he was getting out.

It was so annoying in school all day, though, apart from Conor being back. I got my period and naturally, being me, I didn't have any stuff with me, even though I was positive I was going to get it soon. So I was feeling uncomfortable all day. Now I have awful back pains. Kill me. Please, kill me.

Thursday   *21 May*

I should never have invited a group over to my house this evening. It ended up in disaster. Trevor was upset about his mum, who's dying of cancer, and that kind of wrecked the whole evening, especially Conor, who, being the terrific guy he is, felt the need to be supportive towards Trevor.

Friday   22 May

It was hot today, per usual, so I was actually glad not to go out to yard. We had a short rehearsal during yard time. Alan was out, though, and he has a big role, but Megan was relieved about it – they had a huge fight during rehearsal yesterday.

Wednesday   27 May

I was talking to Trevor today, about his mum and all, because Helen suggested that it might help him a bit, seeing how my dad died, so I've been through it, and I invited him over. We ended up both crying a lot and feeling awkward.

Friday   29 May

There was a disco tonight, as there is almost every Friday night in the community centre, and a group of us went. Half the time we never bother. Funny how two years ago it was considered so cool to be in the youth club and now we couldn't be bothered. Emma wants me to go to Freedom with her, but I probably wouldn't be allowed.

Conor got his cast off and was in a great mood at the start, but then we had a huge fight, but made up at the end. Still, it was totally embarrassing, with everyone knowing about it and trying to be all sympathetic. Conor and I were pretty much the same – we were speaking fine, not sounding upset, but we definitely looked all upset. Our friends were almost acting as bodyguards and diplomats. We both cried a bit, with everyone comforting us – which I wish they weren't. It's nice to have supportive friends, but sometimes you just wish they would leave you alone, because you're embarrassed about crying. Aisling got the picture, naturally, being the terrific friend she is – funny how she picked up on that and not Emma and Orla – and suggested we all leave me and Conor alone for a while, so that we could talk. It worked.

I've been reading over my last few entries. I seem to be doing a lot of crying these last few weeks. I'm going to blame hormones. Conor says he will too. I think that's just 'cause he's embarrassed about crying in front of all his friends. Boys!

Thursday   4 June

Rehearsals are getting to be very monotonous. I know all of my lines now, and if I practise much more they'll lose meaning. At least Aisling isn't making us constantly sing our songs – I think she knows we'll just get bored of them. We sing our songs at every second rehearsal.

Megan and Alan seem to be spending much more time messing than working, if you ask me. I can't exactly blame them, though, if Conor was doing the play I'd be like that too. Still, it gets on my nerves, watching them.

We've sold tickets to almost everyone in sixth class, for the disco, I mean. Since we had to get supervisors, and the

Parents' Association didn't have many volunteers, we had to ask our parents. Emma's mum is supervising – she's dead nice. Emma is horribly embarrassed, of course. Well, so am I – Mum said she'd supervise. I can just imagine it – "Nice children don't do that in public . . .", "Nice children don't do that!", "Nice children wait until they're over sixteen to do that . . ."

Really, I'm not kidding. I know what some kids get up to. Conor and I don't, I mean, not feeling each other (well, not really gross feeling, at least). Sure, we do get off a lot, but everyone does, really, and at least we're serious about each other.

Friday   *5 June*

Mum's plans for our B&B are going as planned. The extension is finished now. We're painting the walls and stuff now. It's fun, actually. Mum let Amy do one of the rooms, and it's great – pale blue walls with all different kinds of stencils in green. I did something like that with my old room, and now it's this really pale purple, so pale it almost looks white, with blue stencils of delicate flowers. It took me ages, but it looks terrific.

Amy is doing quite a bit, now that I think about it. She's volunteered to write out menus in calligraphy, and she's drawn this excellent picture of our house for our ad in the newspapers.

Mum's going to open it on Friday night, the 19th. We're not going on holidays this year, because of how much it cost to do up the house and everything, but she says if we make enough money, the two of us will go somewhere around Christmas. She suggested skiing, I suggested going to London for a few days. That'd be deadly, with all the shops and all the places to see, even if it was for only a couple of days.

Saturday   6 June

I don't know what's getting into me. A few of us were playing tennis on the cul-de-sac road near my house, me, Conor, Megan and Alan. We were playing two at a time, as we only had the two racquets, and Megan was in the process of beating Conor – she's a deadly player – when suddenly I felt so annoyed, from everything to the depressing cloudy weather to the fact that my ankle was slightly sore. Then Alan was joking around, as he was sitting beside me, both of us waiting to get our turn, and I got really giddy and hysterical.

I calmed down a bit when Alan and I were playing. We were tied nearly all the time. Then, when we had just one point to go until we reached the amount we'd decided to stop at when someone got to it, he beat me. So he played Megan, and Conor and I were sitting on the curb, talking. He asked me how the B&B was going, I said it was terrific, and then we talked about the supervisors for the disco, but he sounded so distant. Normally we're really relaxed around each other, but he seemed so tense. I asked what was up and he said nothing. I suppose I have to wait until he tells me.

Tuesday   *9 June*

Conor and I walked home after school, just the two of us.
There was a rehearsal, but Aisling said I could go home,
seeing as there wasn't much point hanging around for ages
until I could do my scenes, and anyway, I knew all my
lines. She knew all my lines by this stage. So I ran out and
tried to catch up with Conor, and he was on his own. He
also looked really depressed, and he finally confided in me.
His dad moved out yesterday. Apparently things between
his parents were really bad over the weekend, and yesterday
things must've just collapsed. He's really upset about it. You
see, his dad's only around thirty-five, and he's really fun.
He was planning to be a supervisor at the end-of-year disco,
actually, if I remember correctly. Anyway, Conor and his
dad do tons of stuff together, and naturally Conor's upset
that his dad didn't even tell him he was going.

He was crying by the time we reached my estate, and I
said, very gently, "Hey, why don't you come inside for a
while?" I was getting the distinct impression he was dread-
ing going home to his mum so upset. He nodded, and I
went in through the front door and we went into my room,
only that sounds very . . . improper. It's the sitting-room as
well, sort of, and the other option was the back room –
Mum's room! Mum was in the new extension part of the
house, so she didn't notice me and Conor coming in.

We sat on the couch for a while, in awkwardness. Then
I offered him some Coke. I had a few cans in my locker,
which is sort of a mini-press, the stuff I put in it. Crisps

165

and sweets and cans of Coke and Cidona, and frozen bottles of water. I love ice cubes.

We were drinking our Coke, with me sipping at it and him gulping it down. I know from experience that if you drink a lot of fizzy or cold drinks, it calms you down when you're upset. And since I froze the Coke last night, it was definitely cold."Are you okay?" I asked him.

"Yeah, I suppose so. I guess I'd better get home."

"Okay. You can come over later if you want, I don't mind."

"Great. Thanks, Kate."

"No problem."

He went home then, and I started on my homework. Mrs Lyons is giving us less these days, whether she realises it or not.

He hasn't come over yet, and it's seven o' clock, so he probably won't. Oh, well. I was playing tennis with Alan earlier. He lives just up the road, and he called down for me to see if I wanted to play. We had fun, he's so funny. It might sound that I'm starting to like him or something, but I'm not, I love Conor, it's just that I needed some cheering up after being depressed by what's going on at Conor's house.

Wednesday   10 June

Well, today was a bunch of laughs. (Heavy sarcasm.) With both Conor and Trevor depressed, I should have insisted on going over to where the others in the class were, telling disgusting jokes.

Both of them were practically in tears. Helen and I were sitting with them, more out of feeling that we had to than we wanted to, and Aisling, Megan and Alan joined us after a few minutes.

I know I should be sympathetic to Conor's problems, and I am, on some level. I just want to make him realise that he can still have a life!

Friday   12 June

The class came to watch our rehearsal, which was during break – it was raining, so we couldn't go out. I was so nervous! I'm starting to wonder why I wanted to get the part. I know I'm going to be a nervous wreck, and I'm going to speak too fast – I always do that when I'm nervous – or I'll get stage fright and not remember any of my lines.

Conor was in a great mood today. I think it was the school tour we had yesterday that cheered him up. I wasn't in his group, but Emma was, and she reported that he had a lot of fun. (And that she pushed him off his surfboard five times, and pushed him out of the canoe twice!)

Our group had a great time as well. Alison was in it, and so were Megan, Robbie, Trevor, and Alan. We made up a team whenever we needed to. We went out on the lake first. There's a village underneath it, but you can't see it, the water's so murky. I was hoping to see the windmill, which is visible when the water level goes down, but with all the rain we've had lately, it was pretty high.

We did canoeing and kayaking. For the canoeing, it was actually two canoes tied together, so we had to break into groups of six. (Which we already were!) During the kayaking, we were messing around as well. I capsized once when Megan crashed into me and another time when I leaned over to talk to Robbie. That time was scary, because it was unexpected and my legs got trapped in the kayak. And, to make things worse, the instructor was rescuing Alison at the time, and couldn't leave her! Robbie pulled the top half of my body out of the water, so there I was with my head sticking out and my arms clinging on to the bottom of my overturned kayak. I wriggled my legs free, and then Robbie capsized – he'd leaned too far over to help me! We were both floating there, laughing, holding onto our boats until the instructor came over to us.

After that, we changed out of our wetsuits, and there is nothing worse than pulling off a tight wetsuit. It's actually painful. Then we had lunch. After that we went orienteering. We had to walk through tons of muck, and there was no way to get around it. After a while, when our runners and the bottom of our tracksuit bottoms were coated in muck, we gave up trying to stay clean and had fun splashing through the pools and the mud. We even started pushing each other in. The muck was like quicksand in some places. Alison started sinking in at one point – the muck was up to her thighs – and Megan and Robbie pulled her out. I rescued her runners, which were filling up with muck. Alison was blushing like mad when Robbie was helping her. She must fancy him. I asked him if he liked her, when the two of us were behind the rest of the group. He shrugged and said, "Oh, come on, Kate, like she'd want to go out with me. She's such a brain!"

I think he's wrong, but I didn't say that. Sure Alison's brainy, but she doesn't make anyone who's not as smart as her feel really thick. And she'd be thrilled if she was asked out. That might sound mean, but I know how it feels to be asked out seriously for the first time. Terrific. The only thing is, she appears so aloof to the rest of the class, and she doesn't even realise that she comes off like that. She's shy, I think, and she thinks no one really likes her except her really close friends. That's not true, they just assume she doesn't like them because she acts so cool to them. It's very complicated.

How on earth did I get on to that? Oh, right, the orienteering. We dropped our map in the muck at one point and we had to fish around for it. Afterwards – we were all like swamp creatures – we threw ourselves into the lake to get clean. So we were soaked, but clean. We had to go back to change before archery. Archery was boring, and it was starting to lash as we were doing it, so it wasn't exactly the high point of the day.

On the bus home, we were all comparing stories. It seems everyone had a great time. Mrs Lyons looked exhausted – like she had a reason to! All she and the other teachers did all day was sit around sipping coffee!

Friday   19 June

The first performance is in five days. I'm so nervous! I know I'll get stage fright! If anyone knew how nervous I was, they'd laugh. Amy and Megan might think they're worried about it, but that's nothing compared to me. I can't even tell anyone how scared I am that I'll do something wrong, because they'll tell me I'm over-reacting, that I'm getting worked up over nothing. They wouldn't understand.

Wednesday   *24 June*

Well . . . I did it and I survived! I was so nervous at first. I arrived really early, when only Aisling was there, double-checking everything. I walked onto the stage, looked at how many chairs there were, lined up, I practically collapsed. I felt tears welling up, and before I knew it I was bawling crying, actually shaking from it.

"Oh, God, Kate, what's wrong?" Aisling asked in that very gentle way of hers. She came over to me and brought me over to the side. She hugged me. "What's up?"

"Oh, God, I don't know, just . . . what if I get stage fright or trip over something or . . ."

"I'd like to tell you that you won't, but . . ."

"Yeah, I know, I know." I sniffed and dried my eyes.

"Look, if you get really scared when everyone gets here, and you really don't think you can do it, remember, I can take over for you anytime you want, okay?"

"Thanks, Ash."

"No problem."

I was petrified when I saw everyone sitting there, waiting for it to begin. But then I peeped out and saw Mum sitting in the second row, and Conor in the fifth row, and I wanted to do it, I wanted to show everyone that I could be a brilliant actress. And I did! I almost messed up for one line, but recovered just in time. It was one of the lines in the argument scene, anyway, so the pause probably sounded planned.

It was great, looking back, of course. I just went out and did it, not letting myself stop to think until the end, when I was like, "Oh my God, I actually did it!" Everyone clapped for ages, so I guess it must have gone really well. At the end Alison and Aisling had to come out onto the stage with us. They deserved it.

Saturday   27 June

The last performance today . . . and guess who had a sore throat? Me. I think it came from when I was at the disco last night, which was deadly, by the way. I walked home afterwards and it was pretty cold by then. And guess who had to step in for me? That's right, Aisling. She knew it really well, and the way she sang the songs was just unbelievable. I'm glad she got a chance to sing her songs for everyone. She created them, it's sort of fitting that she sing them. I mentally compared her singing to mine, and I felt like a crow compared to her! But it's hard to be jealous of her, really, she's too nice. I wish we were going to the same school next year. Still, all eight of us have made a pact still to be friends. And she does live in my estate, so . . .

I'm going to miss everyone, really. Even though Emma and Orla and Amy are going to Hillside Secondary, it's not going to be the same, I won't be in the same classes as them – I found out it goes from F to L, how cruel can you be? Amy is going to be in my class, at least, so that's something to be thankful for.

Claire Hennessy

I've had so much fun this year, with the trip to the Gaeltacht and the play. It's hard to believe it's over. We have two days of school next week and that's it, the end of primary school. We're entering a new stage of our lives. Part of me wants to cling on to memories, another part is wishing I were already in secondary school. I wish there was some way to do both.

5: Megan's Diary

Fact-File

Name:: Megan Walsh

Age:: 11, going to be 12 on February 21st

Family:: Parents divorced, lives with dad

Looks:: Brown eyes, blonde hair, permanent spot on forehead

Hobbies:: Messing around with Amy, going to drama classes

Ambitions:: To be an actress

School:: Hillside Primary, soon to be at Loreto Secondary with Aisling and Alison

Friends:: Aisling, Alison, Amy, Emma

Worst Enemies:: Donna Jones and that crowd

Favourite T.V. programmes:: Friends, Suddenly Susan, Seinfeld, Dawson's Creek

Favourite Actor:: Leonardo DiCaprio – obviously!

Favourite Actress:: Lisa Kudrow

Favourite Film:: Romy And Michelle's High School Reunion

Favourite Book:: Kirsten

Favourite Author:: Elspeth Cameron

Favourite Singer:: Toni Braxton

Favourite Group:: All Saints

Favourite Song:: Never Ever by All Saints

Favourite Album:: Secrets by Toni Braxton

Tuesday   *10th February*

We're making plans to go and see Titanic. Amy and Aisling want to see it because of Leonardo DiCaprio. Alison reckons it'll have a lot of historical stuff in it – she's a real brain – and me and Emma figure that any movie that's grossed hundred of millions has to be good. Plus Leonardo DiCaprio is gorgeous.

Aisling sang the love theme from the film for us – she's a deadly singer. We're both in the school choir but she's always the one who gets the solos.

Sixteen days until the skiing trip in Italy! I can't wait! It's for a whole week, and me and Emma and Aisling are all going. And my twelfth birthday is just eleven days away.

Wednesday   *11th February*

I had so much fun today! We had days like this all the time in fourth and fifth class, but now we're in sixth class, we act cool the whole time. Anyway, today, all the boys started grabbing the girls' hairbands and clips and bobbins and running off on them. Then us girls ganged up on them and chased them around the yard!

I found out that Alan Young is going on the skiing trip. YES! I really really really really like him. And there's a disco over there . . .

I got my passport today. I look so gross in the photo!

Thursday   12th February

Me, Alison and Aisling are fighting with Amy and Emma because they are selfish, thoughtless, immature bitches!

Oh, I nearly forgot. In first yard, before our fight, the teachers made us stay silent for two minutes to pray for peace in the North, the thing the whole country was supposed to do. Anyway, the five of us were standing in a group, whispering a bit, for those two minutes. Then, when we were walking to our lines, Mr. Ruddy tapped me on the shoulder – ME! Why'd he have to pick on me? – and said, "I noticed you and your friends messing around. Have a bit of respect. You know, people are dying up in the North for peace. Did you know that?" Then, just as I was turning around to smile at Emma, you know the way you do after a teacher gives out to you, he swung me around and said, "It's not a laughing matter." Then he left. Me and Emma practically collapsed laughing.

I should've pointed out to him that the more people die in the North, the more fighting there's going to be. He's such a thicko, he wouldn't have thought of that.

Saturday   14th February

We're all friends again.

The disco last night was okay. But A.Y. wasn't there.

Guess who Dad's new girlfriend is? Alison's mum!

Sunday   15th February

Alison came over today while Dad and her mum went out
together. Guess what? She's going on the skiing trip, too!
She just found out. Her mum paid ages ago and has been
kept up to date with the information. This trip is going to
be so cool!

Monday   16th February

Our Ceremony of Light is on the 24th, next Tuesday. We
haven't done any preparation yet in school. Still, I know
what it's about – I'm in the choir and we sang at last year's
Ceremony of Light.

Later

Dad drove the five of us up to the cinema at five-thirty.
We went to McDonald's and then we stocked up on sweets
before we went into the cinema.

The film was great. Leonardo DiCaprio was really good
but Kate Winslet definitely stole the show. She's been
nominated for Best Actress.

Alison and Aisling were crying practically from the start.
I joined in a little while later because the film is just so
romantic and sad. And then there's the music. Amy and
Emma were looking like, "We're so cool, we don't know
these people" when we were crying and then we got really
giddy and silly and were laughing hysterically. Then we
went back to crying our eyes out.

Tuesday   17th February

I got a tenner for my birthday today in the post. Just another four more days and then I'll be twelve.

Friday   20th February

Tomorrow I'll be twelve! I'm having Alison, Amy, Aisling and Emma over tonight. We're going to watch Now And Then, One Fine Day, and Romy and Michelle's High School Reunion. I had a bit of problem convincing Dad to let us watch them because two of them are 15s. I pointed out that they were all 12s in the cinema, (leaving out how Romy and Michelle was actually 15s) and he finally gave in.

Saturday   21st February My 12th birthday!

Everyone's just left. We had a great time. Everyone arrived at seven, and we stayed up for ages watching films. I got some really great presents – including an All Saints CD!

Thursday   26th February

Alan and I are really getting along! He's just in the next room at the ski resort, and he and the other boys he's sharing a room with sneaked in to our room and we had a great pillow fight!

Friday   *27th February*

Wow. I thought skiing would be really hard, but I turned out to be really good at it. At the end of our morning session, me, Emma, and some other kids were put up into the higher group. Surprisingly, Mrs. Lyons is actually a really good skier.

We had octopus for dinner. It was gross. I made up for not eating it by eating everything else, like the bread and pasta.

Our ski instructor, Pierre, is . . . well, he's a show-off, basically. He's gorgeous, but he's full of himself.

Saturday   *28th February*

Does it destroy a boy's ego if a girl beats him at Mortal Kombat? Because I challenged Alan to a game on the PlayStation and I beat him. Then we went into the resort's viewing room – to watch Titanic.

The film got to him. Trust me. I don't care what he says.

Sunday   *1st March*

Ow. I feel really sore. I slipped off my skis this morning, which is probably why.

Today I had a discussion with Alan. Exact words –
"You were so crying at Titanic." (Me)
"I was not. That was you." (Alan)
"At least I can admit it!" (Me again)
"I wasn't crying at it!"

"Yeah, right. I really believe you."

"Another game of Mortal Kombat?"

"Sure. But I'll still beat you."

He beat me this time.

Aisling refused to go skiing today, so it was just me and Alison. (Emma broke her arm yesterday when someone crashed into her). Alison's up in the higher group now.

Oh, by the way, I had another talk with Alan just before dinner as well.

"I am the angel of death and the time of purification is upon us." (That was Alan.)

"You're such a psycho." (That was me.)

"I know. My therapist tells me I need to get it out of my system."

(Laugh) "That's it. You're nuts. Why am I even hanging around you?"

"Because I'm about to ask you if you want to go to the disco with me."

(There's a disco on Wednesday, our last day.)

"Okay, well in that case, I'm about to say yes, I want to go to the disco with you."

(I can't believe I said that so calmly!!!)

"Great!"

Then we went in for dinner. Alan and I sat down together.

"I dare you to eat the octopus." (Me)

"I double-dare you to eat the octopus."

We both laughed, and then we got the octopus. It looked gross.

"You know, tentacles are very nutritious," I said dryly.

The good thing about today was, Alan and I are practically going together. The bad thing was, I had to eat octopus!

Monday   2nd March

Into Milan today for a day of shopping. I spent loads. I bought something for my dad and Amy.

There were some really cool shops – a European shop, a clothes shop for just our age group, and a shop that just sold boxes of chocolates.

Most of us got stuff for Amy. I got her a pair of earrings, which are shaped and coloured like Italian flags. I just hope she doesn't see it like I'm shoving in her face that I was in Italy. Because I'm not, I just want her to experience some of Italy, the way we are now.

Tuesday   3rd March

Only one more day until the disco! I have this really great outfit. Alan is going to go crazy!

Skiing today was okay. Me and Alison convinced Aisling to go skiing again – she hasn't gone since the weekend. We were up on the cable car when she totally flipped out and started crying. I think maybe she was scared of the height, because it was on the first day. Anyway, she had to go back down on the cable car, and me and Alison felt really guilty about leaving her, but she insisted.

Wednesday   *4th March*

God, I feel awful. I've been concentrating so hard on the skiing and Alan that I didn't even notice how upset Aisling is. She actually cried herself to sleep last night. I feel awful. I mean, I'm supposed to be one of her best friends, and I never really noticed how miserable she is. I think she's homesick as well.

I went over to her and we talked for a little while. She seemed to be fine after that, but as soon as she thought I was asleep she started crying again. I feel so sorry for her, but I can't really do anything to cheer her up.

Later

The disco turned out to be disappointing. The music they played was ancient and the amount of chaperones was absolutely ridiculous. Alan and I got out of there as soon as we could and went into the games room. We played on the Gameboys and we watched Ace Ventura: Pet Detective which was one of the videos they had on top of the TV. We laughed over it and then we kissed. Perfect.

Thursday   *5th March*

I can't believe the trip's over. We all had such a great time. I mean, even Aisling and Emma had to enjoy the shopping in Milan and me and Alison enjoyed the skiing.

On the flight back to Ireland, I sat beside Emma and Orla Smith. They were talking about sports, and in front, Aisling and Alison were reading. I felt left out, and you know what? I wished Amy was there then, because we always have a good time together messing around and she always gets my jokes.

At least Alan was sitting behind me. I kept on turning around to talk to him. He's SO funny!

I was just thinking about Amy as I got off the plane and then – it was like one of those scenes from movies – she was there! Really. Emma's mum drove her up and back. I was so happy to see her! I hate to say this, but I'm absolutely sick of Emma and Orla and Aisling and Alison! We've gotten even closer over the last week, but we've also had loads of fights. I don't think anyone has managed to stay out of a fight. I'm so glad to be back and have lots of privacy and my own room!

Saturday   7th March

After Alison's slumber party – which was brilliant – I had to go to drama class. My drama teacher, Melissa, is really nice. I love drama class, and acting. I've been doing it for years. I was in a TV ad a few years ago, and I've done little things like being an extra in some films, and acting in some of the plays the summer community drama class puts on.

Tuesday   10th March

The school hopes to have a play written and ready to perform by the end of June. I'm definitely trying out. It's been ages since I've done anything like this.

Wednesday   *11th March*

Guess which two forty-ish people who work together and who have been going out for only a month have decided to get MARRIED? Yup, my dad is engaged to Lauren, Alison's mum. We're going to be stepsisters!!!

Thursday   *12th March*

Even though Emma got into a big fight today and all that I can't think about that. I got a letter from . . . my oh-so wonderful mother, who divorced my dad when I was barely four and headed off to Paris. She's an actress, which I hate – I mean, I love acting. But I really don't want to take after my mother.

Anyway, here's what the letter said:

Dear Megan,

    I know it will come as a shock getting a letter from me. After all, I haven't written or phoned or visited in eight years. And I'm sorry about that.

    I've done lots of work in films and plays, and I have a lovely apartment in Paris now. Would you consider coming to visit, for a week or so? I'll pay for the flight, of course. I can't wait to see how my daughter's grown up!

    Love,
        Madeleine

I can't believe this. After eight years – EIGHT YEARS! – she writes me a letter saying "Come and visit so I can show off my lovely stuff and how much better my life is now I don't have a daughter".

And the horrible thing is, I can sort of understand how much she loves her life in Paris. I mean, I love acting, and if I had the opportunity in a few years to live in Paris and be a professional actress – well, I wouldn't hesitate.

But then I'm reminded that my mother left me for that. She left her own child to go and do what was best for HER.

Monday   16th March

Oh, I can't believe this (Again). After I made my Confirmation today (I did one solo), a tall, glamorous woman dressed in the latest French fashions approached me. I recognised the face . . . slightly.

"Hello, Megan," she breathed. "You look so grown-up."

That's when I realised that it was my mother.

"I've changed in the last eight years," I said coldly.

My mother flinched. "Actually, your father has sent me photos. I have a lovely one of you in fourth class."

Hear that? Dad has been sending her photos all this time, without telling me!

"Oh," I said.

Dad came over, his arm draped around Lauren's shoulder. Luckily all my friends were off talking somewhere.

"Hi, Madeleine," he said casually, and then introduced her and Lauren as if this was a perfectly normal situation! Honestly!

"Excuse me," I said and hurried off to talk to Linda, a

girl I know from drama classes. I chatted with her for ages, until I was sure my mother had left.

Then I went back over to Dad and Lauren. Alison was standing with them.

Dad slipped an envelope into my hand. "From your mother," he whispered.

I opened it when I got home. Inside was an aeroplane ticket – Dublin to Paris.

Tuesday   17th March

So it's settled. I'm going to visit my mother in Paris for a week. The ticket is for April, over the Easter holidays.

I haven't told anyone yet. Maybe I won't. It's not as if they'll find out. During the holidays most of us are going to visit relatives. I'll say I am – which is true. How much more related can you get than your own mother?

Wednesday   18th March

Alison and Aisling have asked me to help them out with the play. They want me to act out the scenes and see if I think something should be changed to make it sound better when it's actually performed. I agreed.

Friday   20th March

I still haven't told anyone about my mother. I'm keeping busy with helping Alison with the play. Alison, Aisling and I were over at Aisling's house today after school, working on the play, and Aisling wrote this great song. It's perfect for the play, and it's called Who Needs Boys, Anyway? She says she was "inspired" after she and James broke up this week.

Saturday   21st March

Last night there was a disco in the community centre. I went with Alan, naturally. Anyway, I kept thinking about my mother and how it's only a few weeks until I have to visit her for a whole week, and I wasn't exactly concentrating on the disco.

"Are you okay?" Alan asked me seriously.

"Hmm?" I said distractedly. "Oh, yeah, I'm fine."

"Yeah, right. Come on, Megan. What's up?"

"I told you. Nothing, okay?"

"Then why're you acting like a total spacer?"

"I amn't!"

"You are."

"Okay, fine, I guess I am, a little bit. It's just that there's this thing with my mother . . . well, you know how it is."

"Yeah."

I think he really cares, and I would have told him, but I don't think I can! None of my friends know, and I intend on keeping in that way.

Monday   23rd March

None of my friends have noticed – or at least, they haven't mentioned – that I'm being a space cadet. I keep on thinking about – what else? – the trip to Paris.

I've always wanted to go to Paris. But not with my mother! I mean, she abandoned me. I keep on thinking of lots of different things –

1. Maybe I could have been a better kid. I mean, I was only four, but still . . .

2. How am I supposed to keep a week-long trip from my friends, especially Alison, my future stepsister?

3. How am I going to convince Alan that everything's okay? He's noticed how weird I'm acting.

4. How does Dad feel about it all?

5. How am I going to audition for the school play with all this on my mind?

Oh, I hate this so much. Alison will find out – repeat, WILL find out. Her mum is spending tons of time with Dad now. And the rest of my friends will guess. As for Alan, he's going to find out that I don't live with my mother . . . so he'll want to know what I meant when I said "there's this thing with my mother".

And, the school play . . . I HAVE to get the part. If I don't get the part of Samantha, I'll never feel good about myself and my acting ability again. I'd feel like I couldn't act – yes, even after being in that TV ad a few years ago.

The doorbell just rang. I bet it's Alan.

Later

Actually, it wasn't Alan at all, it was Lauren. She's really nice, and I can't wait until she's my stepmother.

Alison wasn't with her. Alison's been working on the play non-stop ever since she was chosen to write it. She really should relax. I think she's doing really well with it

– the play sounds practically professional. I really, really hope I get the part of Samantha. That's the lead, by the way.

There's one thing I'm worried about, though. The singing. Even though I'm in the choir, I'm not all that confident about my voice. Aisling is a brilliant singer. When she sings the songs they sound incredible.

Wednesday   25th March

I leave for Paris early on Saturday morning, and I'll be back the next Saturday evening. I don't know what to tell my friends – we planned on spending lots of time together.

I got a letter from my mother today.

Dear Megan,
    I can't wait until you arrive in Paris! You'll love it, Megan. I must take you shopping for some gorgeous clothes! Megan, please don't feel like you have to love me after all these years. Just try to understand, okay?
    Love, Madeleine

That just made my day even worse. It started off when I woke up with a tummy ache. Then we had choir practice for ages today, and Miss Devlin was really bitchy. On top of everything else, I got my period today for the first time – in school. I would've been stuck except Aisling had some pads in her schoolbag. I think she's already got hers, because she looks really mature for her age – I'm serious, she can get into 15s in the cinema.

Aisling is actually probably the nicest one of my friends. Maybe I can talk to her about my mother.

Friday   27th March

When Lauren came over to see my dad I told her I'd got my period. She was really nice, and said that I'd better tell my dad, which was totally embarrassing! When I told him, he just smiled at me and handed me the money for the stuff and then busied himself with putting away things.

Wednesday   1st April

In yard, everyone was asking everyone had they gotten their periods yet. For some reason, I didn't want anyone to know I had, (Aisling's the only one who knows). Amy and Kate both have – I didn't know that. We've never really talked about it before.

Thursday   2nd April

I have to do a project with Orla. I just hope she doesn't call me over the week I'm gone.

Saturday   4th April

So here I am, on a plane for the third time since Christmas. Only this is to Paris. And I'm going to stay with my mother, who I barely know, for a whole week.

The Easter holiday started yesterday – we got a half-day.

I haven't told anyone yet – I'll deal with that when and if it comes up when I get back.

I'm so nervous about this. Earlier on I was bawling my eyes out over this. My mother. My mother. My mother who abandoned me.

The plane's going to land soon. Wish me luck. I'll need it.

Sunday   *5th April*

I've finally found a use for all that conversation stuff I learn at French class after school. That's the good part.

It isn't turning out as bad as I thought. Yesterday afternoon, when the plane arrived, my mother picked me up. We took a taxi to her apartment. It was SCARY. The driver seemed to be a total lunatic. Then again, everyone was driving crazy.

First of all, she said, "Look, Megan, honestly, you don't have to keep on calling me 'Mother', okay? I don't think I exactly deserve the title. You can call me Madeleine, okay?"

"Okay," I said, and funny enough, it feels much better.

Mother – Madeleine – brought me to a play – which was in English – and she left me in a seat in the first row. I was wondering where she'd gotten to, because she went off somewhere, but then I looked through the programme. She was starring in the play!

She's a brilliant actress. Afterwards, I told her about the school play, a little hesitantly, because she might think it was stupid or babyish, and she was "Oh, Megan, I'm sure you'd be brilliant in it. Chris tells me you're quite the actress. A school play . . . who wrote it? Is it any good, I mean?"

"Alison wrote it. You know, Alison Taylor? She's one of my best friends . . ."

"Lauren's daughter?"

"Mm-hmm."

"Oh, I'm sure it'll be wonderful then. If you get the part – which I'm sure you will – do you think I could fly over and see you?"

"Sure. It'll be on in June."

So that was yesterday. Today we just stayed around the apartment – which by the way is SO classy! – and she asked me about myself.

"I think it might be a good idea to know a bit about my daughter!" she laughed. "Tell me about school, your friends, your hobbies."

"Well," I said, a little shyly, "you know Alison, then there's Aisling, Amy and Emma. School? Mrs. Lyons, my teacher, is okay. Most of the time. As for hobbies? Messing around with Amy. We're the official class clowns. And you know I like acting. Oh, yeah, and I'm in the descants in the school choir."

"Impressive. Boyfriend?"

"Yep. Alan Young. He can act sort of crazy sometimes, like me, but sometimes he can just be so nice and understanding."

"Does he have an older brother just like him?" Madeleine joked.

I looked at her then, and realised how young she is in

comparison to my dad. I mean, he's forty-something, and she's ... let me see, nineteen, and twelve, thirty-one. Thirty-one.

"I'll check!" I returned. "Anyway, let me see, what else?"

"Have you started your periods yet?"

"Mm-hmm. Only about a week ago, actually. And they gave us this talk in school about it, and that sort of thing."

We just looked at each other for a while.

"Did anyone ever tell you, you look a lot like Claire Danes?" Madeleine said suddenly.

"Yes, actually!" I laughed. "Alison had a slumber party last month and we all compared each other to movie stars!"

She smiled. "Sounds like you have a lot of fun with your friends. Here, tell me more about them."

And so it went on, for the whole day, talking.

Imagine having a baby at nineteen. You'd be in ... oh, say, your second year of college. You'd probably still be relying on money from your parents, or else working part-time and making just enough for yourself to live on. Having a baby could ruin the best years of your life.

And my mother didn't give me up for adoption, or have an abortion. She had me and spent four years with me. Which is a lot, when you think about it. In four years I'll be in Transition Year. It seems ages away!

Saturday   *11th April*

I'm back in Ireland. On Monday, we went shopping. I have these gorgeous outfits. I didn't show them to Dad. I don't know exactly how he'd feel. I did tell him about her wanting to come over for the play, though.

Dad has a list of phone messages a mile long. Here they are:

Megan, call me. You know the number. Aisling.

Where are you? Call me as soon as you can. Amy

Why couldn't you make it to the disco? Call me, okay? Alan.

Megan, call me as soon as you get back from your trip. I know about it, okay? So don't try to lie about it, okay? Alison

Did you get me those pictures off the Internet? Bring them over whenever you have time. And ring me! Emma

Megan, CALL me! Amy

Remember, we need to start on that project. Can you call me as soon as you're back from wherever you are? Orla

I was so stupid to think they wouldn't notice I was gone. Of course they would! I tried to convince myself that all my friends were selfishly wrapped up in their own little lives. Too bad all of them had to be so caring!

Finished all my Easter eggs. I only got about six, four from my friends, one from Lauren and one from Dad. I stuffed my face all yesterday.

I'm still avoiding my friends. I ran into Alan on the way up to the shop and he asked what was up, and did I want to break up with him or what?

I said, "Do you want to break up?"

"Of course not. I just thought . . . you know, the way you wouldn't talk to anyone all last week . . ." he mumbled, looking down at the ground.

We went into the shop. It was crowded, so we couldn't talk. We bought our sweets and then walked across the green to my house.

"Look, Alan, I was away in Paris all last week."

"WHAT?"

We reached my house. "Come on in," I said. We went into the living room. Dad wasn't in there.

"I was with my mother," I explained. "Look, remember when I said I was having this thing with my mother?"

He nodded.

"Well, the 'thing' is that my mother ran off on me and my dad when I was four and she came to my Confirmation and she invited me to stay with her in Paris and she paid for the tickets and everything and the worst part is, I LIKED her!"

I started crying.

Alan edged closer to me and slipped his arm around my shoulder. I sniffled and wished I could stay calm for more

than two minutes in a row. It's hormones, that's what it is.
At least, that's what I'm blaming it on.

"It's not a crime to like your mother, you know," Alan
said. "Your dad might be happy that you like your mother,
but also happy that you still love him."

I smiled at him. "You know, you're a pretty sensitive
guy," I remarked.

"Yeah," he grinned, "but don't let it get around. I'd be
ruined.'" He sighed dramatically. "But if it will win the
love of thy lady fair – "

"Okay, now you're pushing it," I laughed.

My tears had dried off by now. We sat there in silence
for a minute. Then we slowly turned towards each other
and leaned towards each other . . . and banged our noses
together.

How do they do it in the films?

Tuesday   *14th April*

Just as I thought I might manage to avoid my friends for
the holidays, Dad reminded me of the Easter camp in our
school. I'd forgotten about it. I signed up ages ago, along
with half my class, and all my friends did as well.

I signed up for drama first, then music, then tennis, then
basketball, and art and crafts. My friends all signed up for
different things, but we all had our lunch together. Everyone who was there from my class was in one corner of the
yard. Me, Emma, Amy, Aisling, Alison, Kate, Orla, Helen,
Carol, James, Conor, Trevor, Sean, Brian, and Ciaran. Alan
didn't sign up.

I couldn't tell my friends then, could I, with everyone there? So I edged away and they followed. I told them all about it, about the trip, about how she's such a great actress, about how I like her.

Some of them already knew. Alison had heard Lauren and Dad talking about it, and worked it all out. And she told Emma. But Aisling and Amy didn't know, and they looked – well, stunned.

They didn't ask why I'd kept it a secret. Just as well, because now I really don't know.

Thursday   16th April

The Easter camp is going fine. Yesterday we went swimming, and today we went on a treasure hunt. I was on a team with Emma, Orla, Kate and Amy, and we won.

Saturday   18th April

It was the last day of the Easter camp today, and we had a table quiz. Helen, Aisling, Alison and I were on one team. Emma, Kate, Amy and Orla were on another one. Conor, Trevor, James and Brian were on another one, and then the other team was made up of Alan, Sean, Ciaran, and Mark. There were more teams made out of people from different classes, of course. My team won, naturally, because Alison's such a brain and Aisling knows everything about music and stuff and I'm practically an expert on films and actors and stuff, and Helen has probably read every book under the sun. We were hopeless at the sports section, though.

Wednesday   *22nd April*

The last few days have been Depression City in our class. Orla and Conor were in a car crash, and no one has heard anything about them, except that they're in hospital.

Kate is acting all cool about it, just like Emma is, and Trevor, but they have to be really upset about if, even if they're pretending they're not.

Alan is kind of upset by it, I can tell, even though he's acting his usual psycho self. Why does everyone have to act like that, putting on a cover-up? Especially Alan. Sometimes I feel really exasperated with him, always kidding around when things get serious, because I know he can be really considerate. I just wish he'd show it a bit more!

Wednesday   *29th April*

I got the part of Samantha in the school play! Auditions were today. And I convinced Alan to try out for the part of Jonathon, the boyfriend. And he got it! He's good at acting, especially acting like he's on drugs – don't get me started! – which is what he'll have to do.

I was hanging around the assembly hall, where the auditions were held, for most of the day. I had to go down at eleven-thirty with everyone else, and Mrs. Lyons looked really annoyed about that, but there was nothing she could do. About ten people from our class went down there.

I had the singing audition first, and luckily the group trying out for the part of Samantha had to go over to

Aisling instead of Miss Devlin. Aisling was friendly to all of us, about fifteen of us.

"Now, I'm going to teach you this song," she explained, "which you'll have to know anyway if you get the part. Now, I'm under strict instructions from Miss Bitch – I mean Miss Devlin –" she winked at me – "to eliminate anyone who can't sing loud enough or high enough or whatever."

I started to get nervous right then, because acting is my strong point, not singing, and there were some pretty good singers there.

"If you get past this," Aisling continued, "you'll go onto the acting audition. And I know some of you have had professional acting experience, so it should be easy." She smiled at me.

She taught us the song, and I sang along with her the second time. The third time, Donna and Hannah joined in.

"Some of you just don't have the ability to sing loud enough," Aisling put it tactfully after twenty minutes. "And for some of you, the song doesn't suit your voices. So only a few of you will be going on to the acting audition. Okay, Megan, you're going through, and the same goes for Donna, Hannah, and Maggie. The rest of you, it's still not too late to try out for one of the other parts."

After that, I had to wait a while with the other three until Alison was finished with the others. Then, just as I was about to go back to the classroom, Aisling told me to stay and help her. "Alison's asked Mr. Fitzsimons and he says it's okay if a few of you stay and help," she informed me.

"Great!" I said, and Kate, Amy and I were hanging around there for the rest of the day. Ah, life.

Later

I phoned Madeleine to tell her I got the part. "Terrific, Megan," she said. "I promise I'll come and see you, okay?"

Friday   1st May

I've done all my packing for the Gaeltacht already. It's going to be so cool. It really is. Dad and Lauren are all, "we're going to miss the two of you" but me and Alison know as soon as we're gone they'll hop into bed together for the week!

Monday   4th May

It's impossible to understand everyone who lives in Donegal. Luckily, at the Irish college, they don't speak the weird Donegal Irish, so that's a big relief.

I'm sharing a room with Orla, Alison and Aisling, and the others are in the room beside us.

Tuesday   5th May

We're having fun, most of us, anyway. The classes are really informal, and we – the eight of us – always sit in a special corner, at the back of the room. We decided that today.

We're doing some great stuff, as well. We've had to talk about the things we normally would, except in Irish, so we were laughing around saying stuff like, "Tá Kate i ngrá le Conor" and stuff like that.

We've tried to plan midnight chats and everything, but mostly we all fall asleep, so there's not much point.

It's weird, as well, being so close to everyone. I mean, I found out that Amy usually puts on mascara every morning. Also, she brought hair mascara, in purple, so most of us have put purple streaks in my hair. If Dad saw it he'd kill me! I did almost all of my hair.

Later

(so late it's actually 2 a.m. on Wednesday)

I'm knackered. I've taken a time-out from our midnight chat-fest to write this. We're all sitting on one of the bunk-beds, some looking down from the top bunk. There are dressing-gowns draped over all of us who are sitting, and Aisling and Alison sitting together under the covers on the bottom bunk, and a few people are up on the top bunk – they keep on swapping every few minutes.

Saturday   *9th May*

Well, we're back home. The coach ride took ages, and we got to the coach late, so we were all split up – me, Amy and Alison in the middle, Orla, Emma and Kate at the back, and Helen and Aisling in the front.

It was a good week, overall, I think. The Irish dancing and stuff was fun, and we had a disco on the last night, which was great. We still ended up doing some of the Irish dancing at it, though, but also showed off our brilliant dance moves. It wasn't like the discos in Hillside, because everyone dances at them, and for the slow dances there's way more people meeting and everything. Still, we had a great time. I wore my Suss bottoms and this great waistcoat thing, over a Miss Selfridge crop top. I looked great. (Especially with all my hair purple!)

Sunday   10th May

Unbelievable. In seven months I'm going to have a little half-brother or sister! Lauren's pregnant. We were over at her house when she told us, and Alison looked as stunned as I am. We're both pretty excited about it, though. It'll be great being big sisters together. I hope it's a girl.

Monday   11th May

Play rehearsals started today, after school. Aisling, Alison, Miss Devlin and Mr Fitzsimons were all there, telling us what to do. We've all gotten copies of the script, and Aisling has typed out all the songs with the music for us to learn, all personalised, so mine only has the songs I need to learn. It must've taken her ages. But that's the sort of stuff Aisling does, she's so nice!

Alison and Aisling took some of us aside, all of us with major roles – me, Kate, Amy, Alan, Brian, Ann Hanley, Carol and so on – and went through each character, so we can get into the role more. Aisling obviously knows how each character is supposed to act, as well, because Alison's descriptions of the characters and the songs for them match up perfectly. I have this great song, Who Needs Boys, Anyway? and when I sang some of it, Alan put on this hurt expression and pretended to be dead upset. But then again, he has a song, Give Me A Decent Girlfriend, so it evens out.

Thursday   *21st May*

Sorry, I haven't written in here in ages. Oh, well, c'est la vie, as the song goes.

My life is ultra-dramatic. Madeleine phoned a few days ago – she's pregnant! Her boyfriend, Kyle Young – not very French, you might think. He's Irish and has been living over there for a few years, but now they want to move back to Ireland – and they want me to be the baby's godmother!!!!

Alison has been asked to be the godmother of our half-sibling. I think Dad and Lauren were going to pick one of us, and it probably helped that I'm going to be a godmother for Madeleine's baby.

"So, your mum's baby is going to be my half-step-sibling?" Alison said. Well, it's something like that, anyway!

Oh, no, I'm thinking about the depressing part of my life now, and any minute I'm going to start bawling. Alan and me had a stupid fight, during rehearsal, and I'm totally depressed over that. So depressed. I'm going over to Amy's house. At least she can cheer me up!

Saturday   23rd May

Alan and I still aren't speaking. It's going to be hard next week with play rehearsals . . . oh my God, I have to do those kissing scenes with him in rehearsal next week! Oh NO.

Friday   29th May

Am I a bitch or what? Listen to this. Alan's still not speaking to me, and I was on my way to the shops tonight when I ran into Trevor, who was pretty upset. At first I thought it was because of his mum, who's got some form of cancer, but then he told me it was because of Helen. Apparently they had a fight – pretty unusual for both of them, especially Helen, since she's so quiet and shy. At least she seems to be, but from what Trevor told me she was a real bitch to him.

Being totally stupid, I suggested we go to the disco to cheer ourselves up, since I was in a bad mood about Alan, still, since I'd phoned and he'd hung up, so we both walked up to the community centre and went in.

We ended up getting off a lot on the dance floor. I don't think anyone we know saw us. I feel horribly guilty now, and so does Trevor. We each promised to keep it a secret. I just hope I can. I don't think anyone noticed – I hope-, because Helen was sick and didn't show up, and everyone was so involved with Kate and Conor fighting . . .

I feel so guilty. We swore it would never happen again. Still, I feel like such a slut.

Tuesday   2nd June

Helen knows! I saw Orla telling her something serious after yard, and I practically had a heart attack. I knew she must've seen us. She shot me an angry look and started crying. I looked over at Trevor and bit my lip nervously. Mrs. Lyons saw her bawling her eyes out and asked if she was sick. I was scared, for one insane moment, that she'd say, "No, just one of my friends meeting my boyfriend, that's all." She claimed to have a headache and went home early. I was kind of relieved. If she'd stayed, Aisling or Kate might have been really sympathetic and she would have blabbed the whole story. Or she might have told Alan. I'm glad she went home.

Wednesday   3rd June

Well, somehow Alan found out, because he was dead annoyed with me today, and wouldn't even speak to me. So, in the half-hour that we had between school and rehearsal (it was delayed because of some staff meeting) and all of us were hanging around in the yard, even those not in the play, and first I talked to Helen on her own, after all, it was her boyfriend, and I felt I should explain to her. I was kind of expecting her to be really mean to me, but she wasn't – she was so nice. She isn't even annoyed with me anymore. I feel guilty about that now.

Then I spoke to Alan, and I told him the truth – that it was because I'd been so annoyed with him that I went off with Trevor, and then I started crying, and I felt awful about everything, and he said, "Oh, stop it, Megan, with that fake crying."

"It's not fake," I sniffed.

"Probably not," he observed. " 'Cause you're wearing black mascara."

We both started laughing crazy then, because I had these black streaks running down my cheeks, mixed in with a bit of green. I don't usually put on make-up for school, just a bit for discos and stuff, but this morning my skin was all smooth and I didn't even any spots, so I felt like making myself look spectacular. Too bad it got ruined, but that's the price you have to pay to get back your boyfriend!

Monday   8th June

I must be insane, putting in extra time voluntarily for this play. I've a feeling everyone is fed up with it by now. We're all nervous, as well, including me. They'd laugh if they knew – me! I mean, I've been in tons of stuff before, but it's different performing in front of your friends, somehow. You feel so self-conscious. At least when you're acting for strangers, you never have to see them again if you mess up.

Our school tour is on Thursday. We're going to Blessington. It cost £15 altogether, and most of us have brought it in. We also have to bring money for a hot lunch there.

Oh – awful news – Dad and Lauren are going to be supervisors at the end-of-year disco! I suppose I'm glad that they offered, because if we don't get enough supervisors we can't have it, but why them? I can imagine Dad looking at me and Alan – "Get your hands off my daughter, young man!" Or worse – "Here's a few methods of birth control – it looks like you'll need it soon!" He doesn't understand that things aren't as they used to be anymore – I mean, I know a girl up the road, she's thirteen, and she's had sex five times already. I know that might be a bit unusual, but still, you know what I mean. I read in those dorky advice-to-parent columns in some newspaper that meeting was considered "sexual activity". Premature, naturally. Get a life!

Tuesday   9th June

I am so bored. There's nothing to do. I've finished making a tape of all my favourite songs – including that deadly one by Aqua, Turn Back Time. Oh, and the B*witched one, C'est la vie. B*witched are brilliant, I think. Except for the Irish dancing bit in the video, maybe.

It's going to be great when Alison moves in. I mean, if we were real sisters we'd be fighting all the time, but as we're just going to become stepsisters, it's new and sort of a novelty. Still, I remember how much we all got on each other's nerves when we were in the Gaeltacht and in Italy . . .

Wednesday   10th June

Madeleine and Kyle both coming for the play, which starts in two weeks. We're doing four performances, and they're coming to the first one, on Wednesday, June 24th. It should be packed. I hope it is, because we need the tickets to be sold to make up for all the money that the school spent on the costumes and props and everything. Also, to have a party for us cast members, and everyone who was involved in it!

Thursday   11th June

Today was great – we went to Blessington for the whole day. It was one of the best school tours I've ever had. Except maybe for the archery, that was boring – we just stood around for ages in the cold until we got a chance to shoot two arrows at the target.

Alan was in my group, which was great, and everyone who was in the group from our class – Alison, Kate, Robbie, Trevor – were messing around with us. We had so much fun, especially with the orienteering – we all pushed each other into the muck! And during the kayaking, we were all ramming into each other. It was deadly.

Later

Madeleine just called, and I was telling her all about the tour. I'll see her pretty soon. You know, she and Lauren are pretty friendly now. Isn't it weird? I mean, you'd expect them to hate each other. They can moan to each other about being pregnant and compare notes on Dad!

Tuesday   16th June

I'm in agony. My period started yesterday. Ow. Why period-stopping drugs haven't been invented is beyond me. This is excruciating! I was going to ask Alison if she had any advice, as she was over at my house with Lauren, but then I remembered that she hasn't got hers yet, so there was no point. Anyway, I felt kind of embarrassed about it.

Saturday   20th June

I'm trying to come up with a list of things I can do over the summer. I know from experience that I get bored by the third week, so it would be nice to think up things to do before I'm too fed up even to pick up a pen and write.

I haven't thought of a lot. I have reading, listening to music, and watching TV down, as well as playing tennis and basketball. That's it. It is going to be one boring summer.

Tuesday   23rd June

The dress rehearsal went really well. I just hope the real thing goes as smoothly . . .

Wednesday   24th June

One word sums up how I feel – wow! It was incredible. With all those people watching – the hall was packed! – it felt amazing, for me at least. It was like I'd never really got into character before tonight, because for the hour and a half we were acting, I felt like I really was Samantha. If you'd asked me my name during that time that's what I'd have said. I was really disappointed when it was over – thank God we have three more performances to go!

Madeleine and Kyle showed up, naturally, and were very

impressed. I could tell Madeleine meant it when she complimented me, and that means a lot, because she's such a deadly actress herself.

By the way, I love Alan even more. We were all so nervous before the play started, including me. Kate was absolutely hysterical, sobbing her eyes out. I felt like joining her, actually, but I kept calm. Alan was just sitting there, in shock, and I went over and asked if he was okay, and I swear, he started crying! I love guys who can actually cry sometimes.

Friday   26th June

Three perfect performances so far. I instinctively know something is going to go wrong tomorrow, but I'm not going to worry about it. It's been terrific so far. There's one scene I absolutely love, the scene in which Alan and I are fighting, yelling at each other, getting really upset, and it gets really tense. It's the sort of thing that if it happened in real life and you were watching you'd wish you weren't there – and believe me, it's happened to me plenty of times! Anyway, I love that scene. Alison had to get us to live sappily every after, though, in the last scene. Alan comes in awkwardly, at the start, and we're all glaring at him, and then I suddenly cave in and we start snogging like mad, and you have Kate and Amy looking at each other and rolling their eyes. It's deadly! Then we all sing Your Friends Are Always There For You, and when it gets to the part where a gorgeous boy is mentioned, Alan always points to himself and grins. It's hard not to crack up.

Later

Just back from the disco. It's the last one Alan and I will be going to together for ages, probably. As I'm going to Loreto and he's going to Hillside, we're not going to be seeing a lot of each other next year. But we didn't split up, we decided there's no point – I mean, I really am crazy about him, and anyway, we live near enough to each other.

We had a deadly time at the disco. I think everyone had a good time, really. The DJ was brilliant, the lights were cool, and thankfully there were no gate-crashers – well, none that could get in, anyway. Dad had to go out to deal with some teenagers at one point. I'm glad I missed it! He and Lauren stayed away from us for most of it. Laura, Emma's mum, came over once, just to remind Emma that she has to be sixteen. (That's all she said. Emma turned bright red. We all giggled, knowing what she was talking about.)

I think everyone danced with someone. Well, except Alison. Which is just as well. My future stepsister may be incredibly brainy, but she still hasn't mastered right and left when it comes to dancing.

Saturday   *27th June*

It's all over. The props and costumes have been stored away, the scripts have been thrown out, everything concerning the play is gone. It feels so meaningless now, all the hard work, all the time after school, now it's just gone. But I suppose we did have four faultless performances – no mistakes four days in a row! Brilliant. I panicked when Kate showed up with a sore throat, but then Aisling took over, and she was brilliant!

We had a party afterwards, which was fun. I was kind of quiet, though. I was thinking about the play and how I missed doing it, and, if we're being brutally honest here, I felt like crying. "Are you okay?" Alan asked me at one stage.

"Yeah," I said quietly. I chewed on my nails. I hardly ever do that – Amy always bites her nails – but I find it useful for something to do if I feel awkward. We went over to a group of our friends who were sitting on the edge of the stage and joined in the conversation. That's the good thing about groups – you can be really quiet or else you can be the centre of attention.

We all got chatting about all the fun times we had in rehearsal, and I wished the song would come true. Aqua, Turn Back Time. That seems to be becoming my theme song. But it's fitting. I do wish I could.

Sunday   28th June

Madeleine and Kyle left yesterday. I'll see them soon, though. They're coming in around mid-July, and they're going to stay permanently. In Hillside, or close enough. It would suit both of them.

It's weird to think that by this time next year, so many things will be different. I'll be finished first year in Loreto. Kyle will be my stepfather. Lauren'll be my stepmother. I'll have two half-siblings, and one of them will be my godchild. Alison'll be my stepsister, and Amy and I will be like strangers by then. I'm not sure I want everything to change, but I can't exactly help it, can I?

Tuesday   *30th June*

Our last day of primary. When I got home I considered crying, but decided against it. I was wearing black mascara, anyway. Today was great – no work, just sitting around the classroom in groups, chatting. Mostly in one large group, actually. We finished at twelve.

It's hard to believe in September we'll all be split up. Most of us have been in this class for eight years – that's two thirds of my life! It's kind of hard to forget that. Add that to the tons of photos I have of me and my friends. Oh, I know we'll still be able to talk and see each other, but it won't be the same. We'll be in two different schools, and in different classes. Only Alison is going to be in my class, and she'll be living in my house as well! I have a feeling we're going to end up fighting a lot. Take when we were skiing in Italy – tons of fighting! And when we were in Donegal, it was the same. And Alison can be really annoying . . .

Later

It's hot and sunny. I was just out playing tennis with Amy. She's my best friend, and now we're going to different schools. Life's a bitch. Well, it's not all bad, I suppose. I mean, I do have two months of freedom ahead of me! Then

Dear Diary

I'll start at Loreto. It's kind of scary, not knowing what to expect. I sort of want to stay in primary school forever, but I know I can't – and I do not like that.

Epilogue: Aisling

Well, I've had nothing better to do with myself, so I've been reading over my diary from the last few years. I found one from last year that really made me feel awful. It was from the Christmas disco last year, the one where we ended up hanging out for half an hour afterwards because of the mistake on the tickets. And it was about Kate. I felt horrible when I read it! She's one of my best friends now, and I hated her back then! I suppose I was jealous of her, really.

It made me wonder, would I have become friends with her if her dad hadn't died? Because that was really when I started thinking of her as a human being with actual feelings, when she came into school afterwards looking really upset. Or would I have got to know her better anyway? When I think about it, every time I've become closer to her, it's been because of something bad – her dad dying, the incident at the party, the accident. Well, there was the play, that was brilliant, so I suppose that's something.

But reading back over my diary – I think I've grown up a lot. Well, I hope I have. And I've had a great time. Well, mostly. Let's not forget that awful skiing trip! Seriously, though, sixth class was really great. We did lots of fun stuff, produced a play, made lots of new friends, and, well, did some things we regretted. I know I did. Meeting Brian was a big mistake. Kevin still doesn't know how serious it really was, but I don't want him to. Some things are better best forgotten! That's from the Steps song, by the way. I got the CD yesterday.

Alison, Kate and I went out together yesterday, to the Square. We ran into Megan with her mother – yes, her mother, she had flown over for a few days, and they looked really happy. Megan looks really like her mum, actually. But back to me, Alison and Kate. We had a great time – we get along pretty well. We all love shopping! Well, window-shopping – we're all broke. Ah, well.

I got a postcard from Amy in Spain! She's having a great time and wishes we were there. Really, she added. Apparently she's very bored and there are absolutely no gorgeous guys around! My heart bleeds for her, I'm sure. She must have a great tan.

Well, now, I'm finished psychoanalysing my life (I swear I can hear a relieved sigh coming from somewhere!) so I'm off to play tennis badly with Kevin in the roasting hot weather. Well, medium-hot weather, this is Ireland, after all. It's quite nice at the moment – by tomorrow it'll probably be raining again. Better make the most of the sun while it lasts. Ice cream, anyone?